Grammar minutes

100 minutes to practise and reinforce essential skills

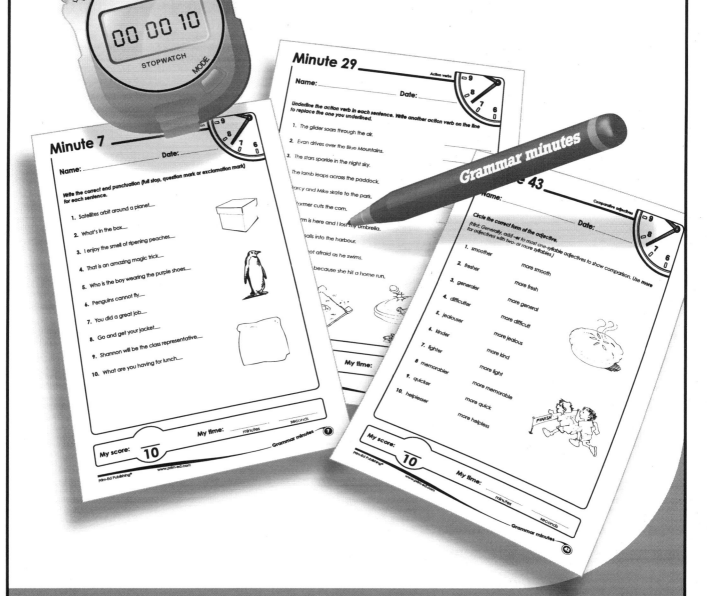

Kathleen Hex

6331

Grammar minutes *Book 5*

Published by Prim-Ed Publishing® 2011 under licence to Creative Teaching Press.
Copyright© 2009 Creative Teaching Press.
This version copyright© Prim-Ed Publishing® 2011

ISBN 978-1-84654-298-5
PR–6331

Titles available in this series:
Grammar minutes Book 1
Grammar minutes Book 2
Grammar minutes Book 3
Grammar minutes Book 4
Grammar minutes Book 5
Grammar minutes Book 6

Internet websites
In some cases, websites or specific URLs may be recommended. While these are checked and rechecked at the time of publication, the publisher has no control over any subsequent changes which may be made to webpages. It is *strongly* recommended that the class teacher checks *all* URLs before allowing pupils to access them.

View all pages online   **Website:** www.prim-ed.com

GRAMMAR MINUTES – BOOK 5

Foreword

Grammar minutes is a six-book series for primary school pupils that provides a structured daily programme of easy-to-follow activities in grammar. The main objective is grammar proficiency, attained by teaching pupils to apply grammar skills to answer questions effortlessly and rapidly. The questions in this book provide pupils with practice in the following key areas of grammar instruction:

- *sentence structure*
- *nouns*
- *pronouns*
- *adverbs*
- *prefixes/suffixes*
- *prepositional phrases*

- *types of sentences*
- *verbs*
- *adjectives*
- *appositives and clauses*
- *noun and pronoun agreement*
- *subject and verb agreement*

- *negatives*
- *Greek and Latin roots.*

Grammar minutes – Book 5 features 100 'minutes', each with 10 classroom-tested problems. Use this comprehensive resource to improve your pupils' overall grammar proficiency, which will promote greater self-confidence in their grammar skills as well as provide the everyday practice necessary to succeed in testing situations. Designed to be implemented in numerical order from 1 to 100, the activities in *Grammar minutes* are developmental through each book and across the series.

Comprehensive teachers notes, record-keeping charts, a scope-and-sequence table (showing when each new concept and skill is introduced) and photocopiable pupil reference materials are also included.

How many minutes does it take to complete a 'grammar minute'?

Pupils will enjoy challenging themselves as they apply their grammar knowledge and understanding to complete a 'grammar minute' in the fastest possible time.

Titles available in this series:

- *Grammar minutes – 1*
- *Grammar minutes – 2*
- *Grammar minutes – 3*
- *Grammar minutes – 4*
- *Grammar minutes – 5*
- *Grammar minutes – 6*

Contents

Teachers notes .... iv – viii

    How to use this book ....iv – v

    Minute records – Teacher record table vi

    Minute journal – Pupil record sheet vii

    Scope-and-sequence table.. viii

Grammar minutes 1–100 1–100

Answers...101–105

Teachers notes

How to use this book

Grammar minutes can be used in a variety of ways, such as:

- **a speed test**. As the teacher starts a stopwatch, pupils begin the 'minute'. As each pupil finishes, he/she raises a hand and the teacher calls out the time. The pupil records this time on the appropriate place on the sheet. Alternatively, a particular time can be allocated for the whole class to complete the 'minute' in.
  Pupils record their scores and time on their 'minute journal' (see page vii).

- **a whole-class activity**. Work through the 'minute' together as a teaching or reviewing activity.

- **a warm-up activity**. Use a 'minute' a day as a 'starter' or warm-up activity before the main part of the lesson begins.

- **a homework activity**. If given as a homework activity, it would be most beneficial for the pupils if the 'minute' is corrected and reviewed at the start of the following lesson.

Grammar minutes strategies

Encourage pupils to apply the following strategies to help improve their scores and decrease the time taken to complete the 10 questions.

- To use strategies whenever possible.
- To move quickly down the page, answering the problems they know first.
- To come back to problems they are unsure of, after they have completed all other problems.
- To make educated guesses when they encounter problems they are not familiar with.

A *Grammar minute* pupil activity page.

Name and date
Pupils write their name and the date in the spaces provided.

Questions
There are 10 problems, providing practice in every key area of grammar proficiency.

Score
Pupils record their score out of 10 in the space provided.

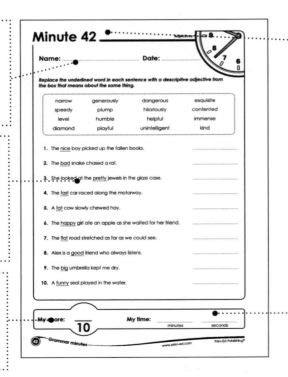

'Grammar minute' number
Grammar minutes are designed to be completed in numerical order.

Time
Pupils record the time taken to complete the 'minute' at the bottom of the sheet. (This is optional.)

Teachers notes

Marking

Answers are provided for all activities. How these activities are marked will vary according to the teacher's organisational policy. Methods could include whole-class checking, partner checking, individual pupil checking or collection by the teacher.

Diagnosis of problem areas

Grammar minutes provides the teacher with immediate feedback of whole-class and individual pupil understanding. This information is useful for future programming and planning of further opportunities to practise and review the skills and concepts which need addressing.

Make use of the structured nature of the questions to diagnose problem areas; rather than asking who got 10 out of 10, ask the pupils who got Question 1 correct to raise their hands, Question 2, Question 3 etc. In this way, you will be able to quickly determine which concepts are causing problems for the majority of the pupils. Once the routine of *Grammar minutes* is established, the teacher will have time to work with individuals or small groups to assist them with any areas causing problems.

Meeting the needs of individuals

The structure of *Grammar minutes* allows some latitude in the way the books are used; for example, it may be impractical (as well as demoralising for some) for all pupils to be using the same book. It can also be difficult for teachers to manage the range of abilities found in any one classroom, so while pupils may be working at different levels from different books, the familiar structure makes it easier to cope with individual differences. An outline of the suggested age range levels each book is suited to is given on page iii.

Additional resources:

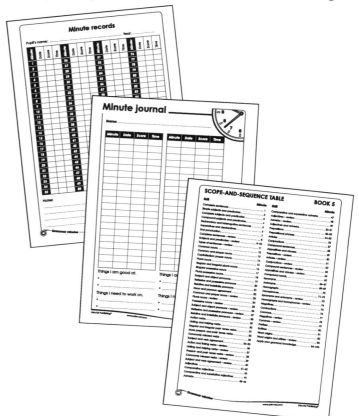

- **Minute records**

   Teachers can record pupil scores and times on the **Minute records** table located on page vi.

- **Scope and sequence**

   The **Scope-and-sequence table** gives the 'minute' in which each new skill and concept appears for the first time.

- **Minute journal**

   Once a 'minute' is completed, pupils record their score and time on their **Minute journal**, located on page vii.

- **Answers to all questions are found on pages 101 to 105.**

Minute records

Pupil's name: .... Class: ....

Minute:	Date	Score	Time	Minute:	Date	Score	Time	Minute:	Date	Score	Time	Minute:	Date	Score	Time
1				26				51				76			
2				27				52				77			
3				28				53				78			
4				29				54				79			
5				30				55				80			
6				31				56				81			
7				32				57				82			
8				33				58				83			
9				34				59				84			
10				35				60				85			
11				36				61				86			
12				37				62				87			
13				38				63				88			
14				39				64				89			
15				40				65				90			
16				41				66				91			
17				42				67				92			
18				43				68				93			
19				44				69				94			
20				45				70				95			
21				46				71				96			
22				47				72				97			
23				48				73				98			
24				49				74				99			
25				50				75				100			

Notes:

....

....

....

....

Minute journal

Name: ....

Minute	Date	Score	Time

Minute	Date	Score	Time

Things I am good at.

* ....

* ....

Things I need to work on.

* ....

* ....

Things I am good at.

* ....

* ....

Things I need to work on.

* ....

* ....

SCOPE-AND-SEQUENCE TABLE   BOOK 5

Skill	Minute
Complete sentences	1
Simple subjects and predicates	2
Complete subjects and predicates	3
Compound subjects and predicates	4
Exclamatory and interrogative sentences	5
Imperatives and declaratives	6
End punctuation	7
Complete sentences – review	8
Subjects and predicates – review	9–10
Types of sentences – review	11
Common nouns	12
Common and proper nouns	13
Capitalisation: proper nouns	14
Plural nouns	15
Regular and irregular plural nouns	16
Singular possessive nouns	17
Plural possessive nouns	18
Subject and object pronouns	19
Reflexive and possessive pronouns	20
Relative and indefinite pronouns	21
Noun and pronoun agreement	22
Common and proper nouns – review	23
Plural nouns – review	24
Possessive nouns – review	25
Subject and object pronouns – review	26
Reflexive and possessive pronouns – review	27
Relative and indefinite pronouns – review	28
Action verbs	29
Linking and helping verbs	30
Regular and irregular past- tense verbs	31
More present- and past- tense verbs	32
Commonly misused verbs	33
Subject and verb agreement	34–35
Action and linking verbs – review	36
Linking and helping verbs – review	37
Present- and past- tense verbs – review	38
Commonly misused verbs – review	39
Subject and verb agreement – review	40
Adjectives	41–42
Comparative adjectives	43
Comparative and superlative adjectives	44
Adverbs	45–46

Skill	Minute
Comparative and superlative adverbs	47
Adjectives – review	48
Adverbs – review	49
Adjectives and adverbs	50–51
Prepositions	52–53
Prepositional phrases	54–55
Articles	56
Conjunctions	57
Compound sentences	58
Appositives and clauses	59
Prepositions – review	60
Articles – review	61
Conjunctions – review	62
Compound sentences – review	63
Appositives and clauses – review	64
Compound words	65
Synonyms	66–67
Antonyms	68–69
Homographs	70
Homophones	71–72
Synonyms and antonyms – review	73
Homographs and homophones – review	74
Negatives	75
Contractions	76
Commas	77
Negatives – review	78
Commas – review	79
Prefixes	80
Suffixes	81
Word origins	82
Word origins and affixes – review	83
Apply your grammar knowledge	84–100

Minute 1

Name: .... Date: ....

Write C *if the sentence is complete or* I *if it is incomplete.*

1. Mum and Dad froze when they saw the mess in the garage. ....

2. Wonder why Jonas pulled the pickles from the shelf? ....

3. The first thing to do. ....

4. The oven was not hot enough to cook the casserole. ....

5. In all of the nicely decorated rooms. ....

6. At the end of the show, everyone cheered for Darla. ....

7. Imaginary lines that run east and west. ....

8. The dress rehearsal for the concert is Thursday night. ....

9. The rooster pecked furiously at the seeds. ....

10. A light in the lonely attic. ....

My score:

10

My time: ....
                              minutes   seconds

Name: .... **Date:** ....

For Questions 1–5, underline the simple subject of each sentence.

*(Hint: The **simple subject** is the someone or something the sentence is about; for example: The neighbourhood **dogs** barked loudly.)*

1. Ella walked to the shop.

2. Giant squid grow 6 to 18 metres in length.

3. The night stars shine brightly.

4. The Petronas Towers in Kuala Lumpur rise over 450 metres.

5. In the office, the phones rang loudly.

For Questions 6–10, circle the simple predicate of each sentence.

*(Hint: The **simple predicate** is the action or linking verb without any other words that modify it or describe the subject; for example: The view **overlooked** the ocean.)*

6. The famous artist Vincent Van Gogh painted *Sunflowers* in 1888.

7. *Up* is Hannah's favourite film.

8. Trees sway gently in the breeze.

9. The Crichton Award is awarded each year to the best picture book.

10. A very sleepy Tyler came down the stairs to eat breakfast.

My score: ___ **10**

My time: ....
minutes   seconds

www.prim-ed.com   Prim-Ed Publishing®

Name: .... **Date:** ....

For Questions 1–5, underline the complete subject of each sentence.

(Hint: The **complete subject** includes all words related to whom or what the sentence is about; for example: A **crowded group of people** stood in line for the bus.)

1. My sister, Lindsey, opened her umbrella.

2. The brand-new building was painted bright blue.

3. Alex's sister sliced the bread.

4. The primary school pupils guessed how many buttons were in the jar.

5. The eager group of tourists watched the wild animals roam around the African savannah.

For Questions 6–10, circle the complete predicate for each sentence below.

(Hint: The **complete predicate** includes all words that show what the complete subject is or does; for example: A crowded group of people **stood in line for the bus**.)

6. Kevin put his books in my backpack.

7. Downhill snow skiing is a fun winter sport.

8. The spring rains helped the flowers bloom.

9. After ringing up my purchase, the cashier politely handed me my receipt.

10. If the conductor is sick, Kate will take her place.

My score: _____

10

My time: ....
minutes   seconds

Minute 4

Name: .... **Date:** ....

For Questions 1–5, underline the compound subject in each sentence.

*(Hint: A **compound subject** has two or more simple subjects with the same predicate; for example: A **man** and a **child** walked down the street.)*

1. Jess and Emmelene wandered through the park.

2. In the garden, roses and daisies were blooming all around us.

3. Jumpers, coats and rugs are often made with wool.

4. The goal defence and the wing defence worked together to keep the ball away from the opponents.

5. The United States, Canada and Mexico are in North America.

For Questions 6–10, write another verb to create a compound predicate for each sentence.

*(Hint: A **compound predicate** has two or more predicates; for example: A man **ate** his sandwich and **threw** the wrapper away.)*

6. Marianna washed the dishes and .... the countertops.

7. The happy babies .... and played in the bath.

8. Victor .... music and played video games on his computer.

9. Owen feeds the horses, chickens, and pigs and .... out the stables.

10. Every morning, I eat breakfast, make my lunch and .... my school bag.

My score: _____
10

My time: ....
                        minutes   seconds

Name: .... **Date:** ....

For Questions 1–4, circle the exclamatory sentence and underline the interrogative sentence.

*(Hint: An **exclamatory sentence** shows strong feeling. An **interrogative sentence** asks a question.)*

1. Look at that! Isn't that a gorgeous sunset?

2. I can't believe I missed the bus! What will I do now?

3. Was that your fastest swim record? It's unbelievable!

4. I can't believe it's broken! How long will it be before we can get it repaired?

For Questions 5–7, insert correct end punctuation for each group of sentences.

5. Oh no__ Sandra hurt her foot__ Should she go to the doctor__

6. Wow, look at the size of the trout__ Is that the biggest fish you've ever caught__

7. Are you ready__ Hurry up or we'll be late__ I think that's the bus__

For Questions 8–10, write an exclamatory sentence to fit with each sentence below.

8. .... What happened to all the peanut butter?

9. .... I can't concentrate.

10. .... It is the best cupcake I've ever had!

My score: _____

10

My time: ....
minutes   seconds

Name: .... Date: ....

Write D if the sentence is declarative. Write I if the sentence is imperative.

*(Hint: A **declarative sentence** is a statement. An **imperative sentence** makes a request or a command. The 'you' does not appear in the sentence but it is understood.)*

1. Use the old stick to stir the paint. ....

2. We are learning the names of past prime ministers at school. ....

3. Draw a straight line from A to B. ....

4. Wear a jumper. ....

5. You are really friendly. ....

6. Lower the volume, please. ....

7. The dangerous substances were locked in Mrs Tipper's science cupboard. ....

8. Use a pointer to indicate the correct coordinates on the map. ....

9. Board the bus before it leaves. ....

10. It is important that the doctor confirms the diagnosis. ....

My score: ___
10

My time: ....
minutes   seconds

Minute 7

Name: ....   **Date:** ....

Write the correct end punctuation (full stop, question mark or exclamation mark) for each sentence.

1. Satellites orbit around a planet___

2. What's in the box___

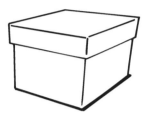

3. I enjoy the smell of ripening peaches___

4. That is an amazing magic trick___

5. Who is the boy wearing the purple shoes___

6. Penguins cannot fly___

7. You did a great job___

8. Go and get your jacket___

9. Shannon will be the class representative___

10. What are you having for lunch___

My score: _____

10

My time: ....
                          minutes   seconds

Minute 8

Name: _____ **Date:** _____

Read each sentence. If it is a complete sentence, add the correct end punctuation mark. If it is an incomplete sentence, write I on the line.

1. Always wear a helmet when riding your bike or skateboard___   ....

2. Our teacher realised we were all beginner violin pupils___   ....

3. The meteorologist predicts the weather with great accuracy___   ....

4. The theatre on City Road___   ....

5. In the past, the fields grew rice and tea___   ....

6. The money in my savings account for a new bicycle___   ....

7. Mr Leonard Wallace Jr, the nicest neighbour on our street___   ....

8. When people enter Australia, they are required to present a passport___   ....

9. All the time___   ....

10. In a seat aboard a private jet___   ....

My score: ___ / **10**

My time: ....
minutes   seconds

Name: .... **Date:** ....

Write S if the phrase is a subject or P if the phrase is a predicate.

1. many people ....

2. build their nests on the ground near a body of water ....

3. is the study of outer space ....

4. painted the ceiling of the Sistine Chapel in Rome ....

5. would be a great adventure ....

6. all of the renewable resources ....

7. as she walked home from school, Taylor ....

8. met at the park to practise for Saturday's match ....

9. Hillary and her family ....

10. escaped from chains and straightjackets as part of his act ....

My score:

10

My time: ....

minutes   seconds

Name: .... **Date:** ....

For Questions 1–5, circle the simple subject and underline the complete subject of each sentence.

1. A virus is a microscopic organism.

2. The great Egyptian pyramids were built as tombs.

3. My good friends, Heather and Tony, were the stars of the show.

4. The bright red robin sat on the branch of the tree.

5. The steaming hot chocolate warmed our chilly bones.

For Questions 6–10, rewrite the sentence to include a compound predicate.

6. Martin walked to school.

   ....

7. All plants use oxygen and water.

   ....

8. My mother curled her hair.

   ....

9. Many Brazilians love to play football.

   ....

10. Rachel strolled along the footpath.

   ....

My score: _____

10

My time: ....
                    minutes   seconds

Name: .... **Date:** ....

Insert the correct punctuation at the end of each sentence. Then write the type of sentence it is on the line. Write **D** for declarative, **I** for interrogative, **IMP** for imperative or **E** for exclamatory.

1. Matter is anything that takes up space___   ....

2. Dad, can you help me build a birdhouse___   ....

3. I won the lottery___   ....

4. Think about it carefully___   ....

5. Did someone lose a jacket___   ....

6. Straighten your tie___   ....

7. Water boils at 100° Celsius___   ....

8. How much money do we need___   ....

9. For the last time, Robert, clean up the mess___   ....

10. The green notebook is my maths notebook___   ....

My score: _____ / 10

My time: ....
                   minutes   seconds

Minute 12

Name: .... Date: ....

Write each noun in the box under its correct category.

explorer	city	bucket	friendship
frequently	love	park	post office
galloped	shouted	biggest	woman
bread	veterinarian	purple	made

Person	Place	Thing
1.	4.	7. ....
2.	5.	8. ....
3.	6.	9. ....
		10. ....

My score: $\overline{10}$

My time: ....
minutes   seconds

www.prim-ed.com   Prim-Ed Publishing®

Name: .... **Date:** ....

Underline the common noun(s) and circle the proper noun(s) in each sentence.

*(Hint: A **proper noun** names a specific person, place, thing or idea.)*

1. Jeff made a lot of friends at Creswick Camp.

2. The glove felt just right to Javier.

3. The match took place at Botanic Park.

4. The pupils learned about the causes of the First World War.

5. Steven mixed all the ingredients together.

6. We met at Nick's house before going out to eat.

7. Our science teacher brought us to Parkes Observatory.

8. Byron Secondary School has a free-dress day tomorrow.

9. The prime minister of the UK lives at 10 Downing Street.

10. They studied the pictures of Venus.

My score: _____

10

My time: ....
                        minutes   seconds

Minute 14

Name: .... **Date:** ....

Circle the proper noun that should be capitalised in each sentence.

1. The official languages in brazil are Portuguese, Spanish, English and French.

2. Did you know that budapest is the capital of Hungary?

3. Millions of chinese people make a living by farming.

4. The Hindu Festival of Lights is called diwali.

5. The eiffel tower is located in Paris, France.

6. The most important book in Judaism is the torah.

7. There are more than 1 billion muslims in the world.

8. The smallest country in the world is vatican city.

9. My friend juanita, who is from Ecuador, is bilingual.

10. The bolte bridge in Melbourne was opened in August 1999.

My score: _____

10

My time: ....
  minutes   seconds

Minute 15

Name: .... **Date:** ....

Write the plural form for each noun.

(Hint: These plural nouns end in **–s, –es** or **-ies**.)

1. shoe   ....

2. hero   ....

3. box   ....

4. skate   ....

5. monkey   ....

6. company   ....

7. princess   ....

8. cherry   ....

9. witch   ....

10. chimney   ....

My score: $\dfrac{}{10}$ **My time:** ....

                                          minutes   seconds

Minute 16

Name: .... **Date:** ....

Circle the two plural nouns in each sentence.

(Hint: There are some irregular plurals in these sentences that do not end in –s, –es or -ies.)

1. The children visited many places on their excursion.

2. They took photos of two deer sipping water from the pond.

3. My grandmother's favourite dishes to make are scalloped potatoes and lemon cream pie.

4. The babies dipped their feet into the paddling pool and squealed.

5. The sheep grazed on the hills, undisturbed by the noise.

6. The paper and pens are on the top two shelves of the supply cabinet.

7. We raked the leaves into big piles.

8. My friends and I get together at the library to study for our weekly spelling and grammar quizzes.

9. Last December, when my mother and I opened the shop doors, we were greeted by elves.

10. Kevin likes horror films, but I like biographies.

My score: _____

10

My time: ....

minutes   seconds

Name: .... **Date:** ....

Rewrite each phrase in possessive form.

*(Hint: Adding **'s** to a singular noun makes it **possessive**; for example: The pencil belonging to Greg = Greg**'s** pencil.)*

1. The web of the spider ....

2. The biscuit belonging to Teresa ....

3. The flute belonging to Kenneth ....

4. The lunch belonging to the pupil ....

5. The stethoscope belonging to the doctor ....

6. The father of the child ....

7. The shoes belonging to Ahn ....

8. The key of the map ....

9. The mascot of the team ....

10. The biography of the writer ....

My score: _____

10

My time: ....
                      minutes   seconds

Minute 18

Name: .... **Date:** ....

Rewrite each phrase in possessive form.

*(Hint: A **plural possessive noun** shows ownership by more than one person or thing. When a plural noun ends in **-s**, adding an apostrophe ['] to the end makes it possessive; for example: The room belonging to the sisters = sister**s'** room.)*

1. The team of the boys ....

2. The lounge belonging to the teachers ....

3. The captains of the ships ....

4. The computers of the shops ....

5. The classroom of the children ....

6. The dresses belonging to the women ....

7. The projects of the partners ....

8. The colours of the leaves ....

9. The harnesses of the oxen ....

10. The hooves of the deer ....

My score: _____

10

My time: ....
minutes   seconds

Name: .... **Date:** ....

For Questions 1–5, write a subject pronoun to replace the underlined word or words in each sentence.

(Hint: A **subject pronoun** *takes the place of one or more nouns in the subject of a sentence; for example: Salim ate hungrily =* **He** *ate hungrily.)*

1. <u>Bill</u> called Conner to ask about the homework assignment.

   ....

2. <u>The girls</u> changed quickly and went swimming.

   ....

3. <u>Stella</u> enjoys listening to music on her MP3 player.

   ....

4. <u>The driver</u> raced around the track at more than 200 kilometres per hour in his car.

   ....

5. <u>Our guests</u> stayed for two weeks.

   ....

For Questions 6–10, circle the correct object pronoun(s) to complete each sentence.

6. Our teacher challenged (we/us) to read 5000 books this year.

7. Will Cathy go with (she/her) and (me/I) to the skate park?

8. The audience clapped loudly for (us/we).

9. The captains selected (she/her) and (me/I).

10. Mark wanted to buy football cards from (him/he) and (me/I).

My score: _____

10

My time: ....

minutes   seconds

Name: .... **Date:** ....

For Questions 1–5, write the correct reflexive pronoun to complete each sentence.

(*Hint:* A **reflexive** pronoun refers to the subject of the sentence. Use the words ending in **-self** if there is a single subject. Use the words ending in **-selves** for two or more subjects.)

1. I will help .... to more cake.
   myself   *yourselves*

2. Each boy should mark .... present on the attendance list.
   themselves   *himself*

3. 'Lauren and David, make sure to pack some rain gear for ....'
   yourself   *yourselves*

4. The car sat by .... in the car park.
   itself   *themselves*

5. The teacher said we can talk among ....
   ourselves   *ourself*

For Questions 6–10, underline the possessive pronoun(s) in each sentence.

(*Hint:* **Possessive** pronouns show ownership; for example: **Our** house is green.)

6. Devon asked Alice if he could borrow her pencil.

7. Ryan drove to my house quickly and parked his car.

8. Whose papers are on this table?

9. Lasagna is a favourite dish of mine.

10. Your birthday is two days before Lisa's birthday.

My score: ____ **My time:** ....
                  10   minutes   seconds

Name: .... **Date:** ....

For Questions 1–5, use either of the relative pronouns who or that *to correctly complete each sentence.*

*(Hint: Use **who** when referring to a person or **that** if referring to an object or animal.)*

1. The customers .... want a bargain will shop at Pick-n-Pay.

2. The lamp .... my brother made is purple and yellow.

3. The pupil .... has a hearing impairment won an award for bravery.

4. The monkey .... ate his hat went to the veterinarian.

5. The person .... is hungriest should eat first.

For Questions 6–10, circle the indefinite pronoun in each sentence.

*(**Hint:** An **indefinite** pronoun does not refer to a specific person, place or thing.)*

6. Anyone can go to the performance on Saturday.

7. There wasn't anything Duncan could have done to prevent the collision.

8. Antonio wants somebody to play tennis with on Thursday.

9. Can everyone see the board?

10. Each of the girls sent a birthday card to Jessica.

My score: ——
10

My time: ....
minutes   seconds

Name: ....   Date: ....

Write the correct pronoun to complete each sentence.

1. Hybrid cars save petrol, but .... more expensive to buy.
    it is   they are

2. Bass and Flinders explored Australia with .... rowing boat, *Tom Thumb.*
    his   their

3. Catherine the Great, Empress of Russia, expanded .... empire during her reign.
    her   their

4. Anybody who loses .... ticket will not be admitted to the show.
    their   his

5. Both boys practised .... penalty kicks each night.
    their   his

6. Something under the bed moved .... fluffy tail.
    its   their

7. People should brush .... teeth twice a day.
    their   her

8. Electricians must complete extensive training before doing a job on

    .... own.
    their   her

9. Campers should be especially careful when .... near a river.
    they are   she is

10. The first time Wes and Quang went bowling, ... each scored over one hundred points.
    they   he

My score: _____
10

My time: ....
minutes   seconds

Name: ....

Date: ....

Underline the common noun(s) and circle the proper noun(s) in each sentence.

1. When Charlene is hungry, she makes a sandwich.

2. The guitar was less expensive at Melody Music Shop.

3. Parker's birthday is 27 January.

4. The Tour de France is a bicycle race through France.

5. Let's meet at the cinema on Monday.

6. A squirrel raced through the trees in Highland Park.

7. My apartment is on the third floor.

8. Louise asked the banker for a loan.

9. The Statue of Liberty is in New York City.

10. Please take the rubbish out.

My score: ___
10

My time: ....
minutes   seconds

Minute 24

Name: .... **Date:** ....

For Questions 1–5, read the paragraph and circle the five plural nouns. Write them on the lines.

The climbers set off to reach the summit of Mt Kilimanjaro. They carried knives, cooking utensils and food with them. It would take a long time to reach the top and set up camp. They had been training for months with people around the area. What a victory it would be to finally reach their destination!

1. ....

2. ....

3. ....

4. ....

5. ....

For Questions 6–10, write the plural form for each noun.

6. beetle ....

7. hobby ....

8. mouse ....

9. half ....

10. echo ....

My score: ___ **10**

My time: ....
minutes   seconds

www.prim-ed.com   Prim-Ed Publishing®

Minute 25

Name: .... **Date:** ....

For Questions 1–5, rewrite each phrase in possessive form.

1. The department for men

   ....

2. The bookshelf belonging to Cindy

   ....

3. The windows of the galleries

   ....

4. The crayons belonging to the toddler

   ....

5. The water bottles belonging to the runners

   ....

For Questions 6–10, underline the singular possessive phrase and circle the plural possessive phrase in each sentence.

6. Melissa's motorcycle ran more smoothly than her friends' motorcycles.

7. The Dolphins' victory made Dad's day.

8. The flowers' pollen affected Jessica's allergies.

9. I don't like to walk to Daria's Grocery Store because of the neighbourhood dogs' loud barking as I enter their territory.

10. Lisa's pet hamster can't climb onto the sofas' slippery cushions.

My score: _____

10

My time: ....

minutes   seconds

Name: .... **Date:** ....

For Questions 1–5, circle the correct object pronoun(s) to complete each sentence.

1. Mum made lasagna for my brother and (me/I).

2. Mrs Green chose Warren and (she/her) to finish the maths problems on the board.

3. The puppy followed (they/them) home from the park.

4. The calculators belong to (she/her) and (he/him).

5. Lisa asked (he/him) and (I/me) to go to the cinema.

For Questions 6–10, write a subject pronoun to replace the underlined word or words in each sentence.

6. Ronald appears in many television commercials. ....

7. The turtle sunned itself on the rocks. ....

8. Air pollution is hazardous to the Earth and to humans' health. ....

9. The twins will receive an award for their volunteer work at the daycare centre. ....

10. Erin and I earn money by mowing our neighbours' lawns. ....

My score: ____

10

My time: ....
minutes   seconds

Minute 27

Name: ....   **Date:** ....

For Questions 1–5, write the correct possessive pronoun to complete each sentence.

1. When Jenna's baby brother laughs, ... new baby teeth show.

2. .... neighbour's house has lights that turn off automatically.

3. Trent and Carla are working on .... project.

4. Even though Liz said she wasn't good at bowling, I found out .... top score in bowling is 219.

5. We could hardly believe .... eyes.

For Questions 6–10, write the correct reflexive pronoun from the box to complete each sentence.

themselves	herself	himself	itself	yourself

6. Henry built a treehouse all by ....

7. Kenlyn ate a meat pie, but Sarah made a salad for ....

8. He and his friends bought concert tickets for ....

9. You should drive to the market by ....

10. A gecko can grow .... a new tail.

My score: ____
10

My time: ....
minutes   seconds

Name: ....   **Date:** ....

For Questions 1–5, circle the correct relative pronoun to complete each sentence.

1. Mother Teresa was a woman (who/that) served the poor her entire life.

2. The antique chair (who/that) belongs to my mother is a family heirloom.

3. Belinda has a favourite hat (who/that) once belonged to her sister.

4. The television (who/that) has loud speakers is better for playing video games.

5. The person in the drama club (who/that) raises the most money for the trip will win a prize.

For Questions 6–10, write yes if the indefinite pronoun in the phrase is used correctly. Write no if it is not.

6. Many of the pupils put his backpacks under the desks.   ....

7. Either boy can drive his truck.   ....

8. Someone brought their skateboard into the house.   ....

9. Does everyone have their homework finished?   ....

10. Both of the boys received telescopes for their birthdays.   ....

My score: _____
10

My time: ....
minutes   seconds

Name: .... **Date:** ....

Underline the action verb in each sentence. Write another action verb on the line to replace the one you underlined.

1. The glider soars through the air.   ....

2. Evan drives over the Blue Mountains.   ....

3. The stars sparkle in the night sky.   ....

4. The lamb leaps across the paddock.   ....

5. Marcy and Mike skate to the park.   ....

6. The farmer cuts the corn.   ....

7. The storm is here and I lost my umbrella.   ....

8. The boat sails into the harbour.   ....

9. The diver is not afraid as he swims.   ....

10. Helen is happy because she hit a home run.   ....

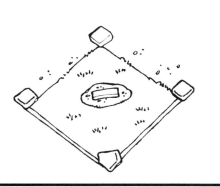 

My score: _____
10

My time: ....
minutes   seconds

Name: .... **Date:** ....

For Questions 1–5, underline the linking verb in each sentence.

*(Hint: A **linking verb** does not express action. It connects the subject to the rest of the information about the subject.)*

1. That octopus is large and scary.

2. I am sleepy after my long trip.

3. Apples are my favourite fruit.

4. The animals in the zoo are interesting to watch.

5. The aeroplanes were all late because of the storm.

For Questions 6–10, circle the sentence in each pair that has a helping verb.

*(Hint: A **helping verb** is the first word of a verb phrase and often sets the time and mood.)*

6. (a) She will go to the cinema with Brenda.

   (b) She watched the film with Brenda.

7. (a) Janice and Nicola helped their mother with the cooking.

   (b) Janice and Nicola are helping their mother cook.

8. (a) We meet to play football on Wednesday.

   (b) We have been playing football for an hour.

9. (a) She is nice.

   (b) She is acting nice.

10. (a) I am going to my house.

    (b) I want to go home.

My score: ____
10

My time: ....
minutes   seconds

Minute 31

Name: .... **Date:** ....

Write the past-tense forms of each verb below.

(Hint: Not all past-tense verbs end in **–ed**.)

Present tense	Past tense
1. sail	....
2. scream	....
3. fly	....
4. answer	....
5. grow	....
6. act	....
7. wear	....
8. write	....
9. boil	....
10. break	....

My score: $\frac{\quad\quad}{10}$

My time: ....

minutes   seconds

Minute 32

Name: .... **Date:** ....

Add –ed or –ing to the verb to correctly complete each sentence.

1. Who .... the internet?
   invent

2. The lionesses .... in the cool hours of the evening.
   hunt

3. Travis was .... about his bicycle tricks.
   joke

4. Mrs Jones .... there would be an English test on Thursday.
   mention

5. Thousands of people are .... to warmer locations.
   move

6. The sporting goods store is .... a discount for frequent shoppers.
   offer

7. The queen .... the country for more than 40 years.
   rule

8. Shelly is .... a surprise birthday party for her mother.
   plan

9. The workers are .... the produce for the restaurant.
   unload

10. Aunt Betsy is .... from Spain for a week.
    visit

My score: ___ **My time:** ....
     10   minutes   seconds

Name: .... Date: ....

For Questions 1–5, circle the correct verb to complete each sentence.

*(Hint: The verbs **lay, set** and **raise** are used with a direct object.)*

1. Please (lay/lie) the books on the table.

2. Robert (lies/lays) on the sofa because he isn't feeling well.

3. Mr Henderson (set/sit) the microscopes on the tables.

4. We taught our dog to (sit/set) on command.

5. The hills (rise/raise) above the valley.

For Questions 6–10, write the correct past-tense verb on the line.

6. Ms Fortunato .... the curtain and the show began.
   raised   rose

7. Yesterday, the cat .... in the sunshine on the porch.
   lay   laid

8. Jasmine .... the plates around the table.
   past   passed

9. We each .... at a computer station in the library.
   sat   set

10. I always .... my library card right on the counter.
    lay   lie

My score: _____

10

My time: ....
                  minutes   seconds

Minute 34

Name: .... **Date:** ....

For Questions 1–5, write the correct form of the verb to complete each phrase.

Example: Wait

I wait

You wait

He waits

They wait

1. Laugh

I ....

You ....

She ....

They ....

2. Ask

I ....

You ....

She ....

They ....

3. Start

I ....

You ....

She ....

They ....

4. Paint

I ....

You ....

She ....

They ....

5. Dance

I ....

You ....

She ....

They ....

For Questions 6–10, circle the correct verb form to complete each sentence.

6. Jerry and June (mops/mop) the floor.

7. Class 5 (plant/plants) a tree every year.

8. The bee (stings/sting) the predator who threatens it.

9. He (turn/turns) off the light when leaving the room.

10. Fran (ignore/ignores) the telephone while she is studying.

My score: _____
10

My time: ....
        minutes   seconds

Minute 35

Name: .... Date: ....

Circle the correct verb form to complete each sentence.

1. Our cricket team (is/are) the best in the town.

2. The class (earn/earns) a reward for each cake sale item sold.

3. The number of people who like brussels sprouts (is/are) very small.

4. The hills (is/are) gleaming with white snow.

5. Doctors (is/are) very caring people.

6. Chandra's glasses (is/are) on her desk.

7. Ronald and Jan (is/are) playing badminton.

8. Either William's brother or my mum (drive/drives) us to school.

9. Neither Chris nor James will (wear/wears) braces anymore.

10. The scissors (is/are) in the top drawer.

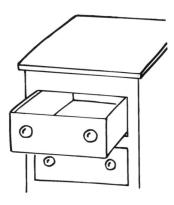

My score: _____
   10

My time: ....
              minutes   seconds

Minute 36

Name: .... **Date:** ....

For Questions 1–5, either circle the action verb or underline the linking verb in each sentence.

1. The roller-coaster raced around the track.

2. A sandcastle collapses in the surf.

3. Natalie was fourteen years old.

4. Pete and Bruce built a go-kart from scraps of wood.

5. He is very tired.

For Questions 6–10, write a sentence that includes an action verb.

6. It is raining outside.

   The rain ....

7. It is nice weather in the city today.

   The sun ....

8. My friend and I had fun at the concert.

   My friend and I ....

9. Lisa is tired.

   Lisa ....

10. I am hungry.

    My stomach ....

My score: $\overline{}$
10

My time: ....
                  minutes   seconds

www.prim-ed.com   Prim-Ed Publishing®

Name: .... **Date:** ....

Write **H** *if the verb in the sentence helps another verb or expresses time or mood. Write* **L** *if the verb links two ideas together.*

1. I will run to the shop quickly. ....

2. The capital of Thailand is Bangkok. ....

3. The peaches are ripe. ....

4. The bananas will ripen if you store them in a paper bag. ....

5. They should walk to the cinema rather than drive. ....

6. He is taking his time. ....

7. The shoes were in the wardrobe. ....

8. He can store his shoes in the wardrobe. ....

9. The evening sky is beautiful. ....

10. The chef seems capable. ....

My score: ____

$\frac{}{10}$

My time: ....

minutes   seconds

Minute 38

Name: .... **Date:** ....

For Questions 1–5, write the past-tense form of each verb.

1. run   ....

2. dive   ....

3. freeze   ....

4. walk   ....

5. think   ....

For Questions 6–10, add –ing or –ed to the verb to correctly complete each sentence.

6. Janice is .... the crumbs that fell on the floor.
        sweep

7. When the glue has ...., we can take home our projects.
        dry

8. The drummers are .... in a parade this Saturday.
        march

9. All of the athletes .... after completing the race.
        stretch

10. The fireworks .... in the sky.
        explode

My score: _____
10

My time: ....
                  minutes   seconds

www.prim-ed.com   Prim-Ed Publishing®

Name: .... **Date:** ....

For Questions 1–5, circle the correct verb to complete each sentence.

1. Where did you (lay/lie) the pencils?

2. It feels good to (lie/lay) down after a long bike ride.

3. Jimmy likes to (set/sit) out all his materials before he paints.

4. Mum honked the car horn as we (passed/past) the school.

5. The class will (rise/raise) money to go on an excursion.

For Questions 6–10, write yes if the correct verb is used for each sentence. Write no if it is not.

6. We passed time by playing road trip games.   ....

7. The bread will raise to the top of the pan.   ....

8. I lie the presents on the table.   ....

9. The vase sits on the mantle in our living room.   ....

10. After you're finished reading the newspaper, sit it on the shelf.   ....

My score:

10

My time: ....

minutes   seconds

Name: .... **Date:** ....

Circle the correct verb form to complete each sentence.

1. Candice (expect/expects) her team to win the competition.

2. The tired old dog (flop/flops) down on the kitchen floor.

3. There (was/were) too many pupils standing in the hallway.

4. In my grandfather's attic (is/are) dozens of old cameras.

5. Bianca, my older sister, (plan/plans) to attend Edinburgh in the autumn.

6. The flesh of the fruit (is/are) tender and juicy.

7. Harry (wish/wishes) his best friend would get well soon.

8. The teacher (eat/eats) in the school dining room along with his pupils.

9. Among the top three tennis players in the world (is/are) two Europeans and one Canadian.

10. The adventurous climber (use/uses) ropes and other safety devices as she climbs the face of the cliff.

My score: _____

10

My time: ....
                minutes   seconds

Minute 41

Name: .... **Date:** ....

For Questions 1–5, circle the descriptive adjective(s) in each sentence.

1. The awkward foal returned to the barn.

2. The magic carpet flew over the city.

3. The baker delivered delicious biscuits for the teachers' meeting.

4. A tiny, black puppy romped in the white snow.

5. The dirty, smelly shoes were left on the step.

For Questions 6–10, use an adjective from the box to best complete each sentence.
Use each adjective only once.

demanding	little	green
beautiful	unpredictable	mashed

6. The .... volcano finally erupted last week.

7. Anne is saving her money to buy a .... necklace.

8. The .... passenger asked the driver to listen to his directions.

9. Kevin's .... brother likes .... balloons.

10. The restaurant is serving .... potatoes for lunch today.

My score:

10

My time: ....
minutes   seconds

Minute 42

Name: .... **Date:** ....

Replace the underlined word in each sentence with a descriptive adjective from the box that means about the same thing.

narrow	generously	dangerous	exquisite
speedy	plump	hilariously	contented
level	humble	helpful	immense
diamond	playful	unintelligent	kind

1. The <u>nice</u> boy picked up the fallen books. ....

2. The <u>bad</u> snake chased a rat. ....

3. She looked at the <u>pretty</u> jewels in the glass case. ....

4. The <u>fast</u> car raced along the motorway. ....

5. A <u>fat</u> cow slowly chewed hay. ....

6. The <u>happy</u> girl ate an apple as she waited for her friend. ....

7. The <u>flat</u> road stretched as far as we could see. ....

8. Alex is a <u>good</u> friend who always listens. ....

9. The <u>big</u> umbrella kept me dry. ....

10. A <u>funny</u> seal played in the water. ....

My score: ___
10

My time: ....
minutes   seconds

Minute 43

Name: .... **Date:** ....

Circle the correct form of the adjective.

*(Hint: Generally, add –er to most one-syllable adjectives to show comparison. Use **more** for adjectives with two- or more syllables.)*

1. smoother   more smooth

2. fresher   more fresh

3. generaler   more general

4. difficulter   more difficult

5. jealouser   more jealous

6. kinder   more kind

7. lighter   more light

8 memorabler   more memorable

9. quicker   more quick

10. helplesser   more helpless

My score: $\dfrac{\quad}{10}$

My time: ....
                minutes   seconds

Minute 44

Name: ....   **Date:** ....

For Questions 1–5, circle the correct adjective to complete each sentence.

1. Mint chocolate chip is the (good/best) ice-cream flavour available.

2. A broken leg is (worse/more bad) than a broken fingernail.

3. Sharice picked (most/more) berries than Frank.

4. That film was (less/least) exciting than the one we saw last week.

5. The sour pickles were (more worse/worse) than the lemons.

For Questions 6–10, write the comparative and superlative form of each adjective.

Adjective	Comparative	Superlative
e.g. high	higher	highest
6. flat	....	....
7. brave	....	....
8. strong	....	....
9. calm	....	....
10. lean	....	....

My score: ____
10

My time: ....
                              minutes   seconds

www.prim-ed.com   Prim-Ed Publishing®

Minute 45

Name: .... **Date:** ....

For Questions 1–5, circle the adverb in each sentence.

*(Hint: An **adverb** is a word that tells **how, when** or **where** something happens.)*

1. The team played mightily but lost the football match.

2. The boulder landed heavily on the valley floor.

3. Trisha waited eagerly while her mother paid for the new dress.

4. Measure exactly how long the shelf should be.

5. The spinning top twirled crazily before falling off the table.

For Questions 6–10, circle the correct use of good or well in each sentence.

*(Hint: Use **good** as an adjective; for example: She is having a good day. Use **well** as an adverb; for example: She draws well.)*

6. The chocolate cupcakes smell (good/well).

7. Kate played (good/well) in the game.

8. The knots in the line look (good/well).

9. Nadia danced (good/well) at her ballet recital.

10. Hee-Jin did (good/well) on her science test.

My score:

10

My time: ....
minutes   seconds

Minute 46

Name: .... **Date:** ....

Write how, when, where, how often or to what degree to tell what the underlined adverb describes.

1. The pupils worked <u>quickly</u>.

   ....

2. Drake visits his grandmother <u>frequently</u>.

   ....

3. Mr Rodriguez finds teaching <u>extremely</u> enjoyable.

   ....

4. Grace will start secondary school <u>next</u> year.

   ....

5. You left your lunch <u>there</u> on the table.

   ....

6. I am leaving <u>today</u> for choir camp.

   ....

7. Julie worked <u>carefully</u> on her egg decorating.

   ....

8. The doctor pressed <u>gently</u> on Sara's broken arm.

   ....

9. Ms Muldoon checks our homework <u>daily</u>.

   ....

10. Josh was <u>very</u> grateful when his wallet was found.

    ....

My score: _____

10

My time: ....
           minutes   seconds

Name: .... **Date:** ....

For Questions 1–10, write the comparative and superlative form of each adverb.

(Hint: Use either **–er** and **–est** or **more** and **most**.)

Adverb	Comparative	Superlative
1. fast	....	....
2. quietly	....	....
3. early	....	....
4. often	....	....
5. slowly	....	....
6. far	....	....
7. near	....	....
8. carefully	....	....
9. soon	....	....
10. gracefully	....	....

My score: ___
10

My time: ....
minutes   seconds

Minute 48

Name: .... Date: ....

For Questions 1–5, circle the correct form of the adjective to complete each sentence.

(Hint: Adjectives that end in –er compare two things and adjectives that end in –est compare more than two things.)

1. Mrs Klein's maths class is (more hard/harder) than Mr. Brown's.

2. My scoop of ice-cream is (larger/largest) than Tommy's.

3. The drum is (more louder/louder) than the guitar.

4. Danielle is the (more smaller/smallest) of the triplets.

5. Of all the pupils in the class, Gabriel is the (most tallest/tallest).

For Questions 6–10, write the comparative or superlative form of each adjective.

Adjective	Comparative	Superlative
6. good	better	....
7. bad	....	worst
8. little	less	....
9. few	....	fewest
10. much	more	....

My score: _____
10

My time: ....
minutes   seconds

Minute 49

Name: .... **Date:** ....

Circle the word that the underlined adverb modifies.

*(Hint: An **adverb** can modify a verb, an adjective or another adverb.)*

1. We <u>hesitantly</u> ate the okra Mum served us.

2. The mother chimpanzee held her baby <u>snugly</u> against her chest.

3. We <u>often</u> go to the swimming pool at the community centre.

4. Contests are held <u>locally</u> for anyone who is interested.

5. Javier <u>thoughtfully</u> considered his options before deciding.

6. The strangely shaped teddy bear sat <u>awkwardly</u> on the shelf in the toy shop.

7. The guests spoke <u>loudly</u> in the dining room.

8. Sasha marched <u>purposefully</u> to the teacher's desk.

9. Mrs Westland is <u>very</u> generous.

10. I will remember this holiday <u>forever</u>.

My score: _____

10

My time: ....
                                            minutes   seconds

Name: ....   **Date:** ....

Write adj if the word underlined is an adjective or adv if the word underlined is an adverb.

1. Runs <u>quickly</u>   ....

2. <u>Playful</u> puppy   ....

3. Gaze <u>longingly</u>   ....

4. <u>Cold</u> water   ....

5. Eat <u>frequently</u>   ....

6. Speak <u>quietly</u>   ....

7. <u>Quiet</u> pupils   ....

8. <u>Fried</u> chicken   ....

9. <u>Hard</u> rock   ....

10. <u>Hardly</u> working   ....

My score: $\dfrac{}{10}$ **My time:** ....

minutes   seconds

Name: .... **Date:** ....

Circle the word(s) the underlined adjective or adverb modifies.

1. The brilliant blue chair is the <u>most uncomfortable</u> seat in the room.

2. The moon shone <u>brightly</u> over the majestic mountains.

3. We had an <u>incredible</u> view from the window of our cabin.

4. The drum beat a <u>contagious</u> rhythm.

5. Mum says the washing machine runs <u>constantly</u>.

6. There were <u>subtle</u> signs Ernie was planning a party.

7. Wendy <u>effortlessly</u> climbed the rock wall.

8. The player bounced the ball <u>repeatedly</u> before taking a shot.

9. Our group worked <u>hard</u> on the science project.

10. Zack is the most <u>experienced</u> traveller in the group.

My score: ____

10

My time: ....
minutes   seconds

Minute 52

Name: .... **Date:** ....

For Questions 1–5, circle the two prepositions in each sentence.

*(Hint: A **preposition** shows a relationship of a noun or pronoun to another word in the sentence and often tells where, what kind, when or how; for example: I ran **along** the shore.)*

1. Roland had to choose between the frill-necked lizard and the green iguana as his pet.

2. The palaeontologist with the white gloves placed the fossil inside the heavy glass case.

3. The two girls looked at each other across the table.

4. Our football team celebrated at a restaurant after winning the grand final.

5. The pepper tree beside the brook up the road is my favourite place to read.

For Questions 6–10, use a preposition from the box to correctly complete each sentence. Use each preposition only once.

inside	beneath	with	since	near

6. The pupils put their lunch boxes .... their lockers.

7. The cave .... the mouth of the river was full of bats.

8. Magma forms well .... the earth's surface.

9. The little boat .... a striped sail won the race.

10. .... she discovered stamp collecting, Sara has given up gardening.

My score: _____
10

My time: ....
minutes   seconds

Minute 53

Name: .... **Date:** ....

For Questions 1–5, write between or among to correctly complete each sentence.

*(Hint: Use **between** when you are referring to two people, items or ideas; use **among** when referring to three or more.)*

1. The contest is .... Shana and Jamila.

2. Who .... you is the greatest warrior?

3. I had to choose .... chocolate chip and vanilla ice-cream.

4. Isabella finished her homework .... seven and eight o'clock.

5. Voters will decide .... the two candidates.

For Questions 6–10, write yes if the correct preposition is used. Write no if it is not.

6. How many towns are <u>among</u> Humpty Doo and Jabiru? ....

7. Quan, Fran and David are <u>among</u> the favourites to win the golf tournament. ....

8. Mrs Sanger will choose <u>among</u> the Mighty Mongrels and the Laughing Labradors for the winner of the talent show. ....

9. My coach is the woman standing <u>between</u> the two men in red jackets. ....

10. Choosing a book <u>between</u> so many great titles is difficult. ....

My score: ____

10

My time: ....
minutes   seconds

Name: .... **Date:** ....

Circle either a or b to show which underlined phrase is the prepositional phrase in each sentence.

(Hint: A **prepositional phrase** begins with a preposition and ends with a noun.)

1. In India, tigers can be found roaming in the wild.
   a   b

2. The school counsellor encouraged us to think about our future career choices.
          a   b

3. Jimmy had trained for the X Games in snowboarding.
        a   b

4. John Curtin had many accomplishments as a great Australian leader.
          a   b

5. In 1957, the Soviet Union launched its first successful satellite, _Sputnik 1._
   a   b

6. Now happy, Carla skipped off with her best friend, Janelle.
       a   b

7. In live concert, Ian's favourite band was even better.
       a   b

8. Neptune takes more than 165 years to revolve around the sun.
              a   b

9. Tropical rainforests have the greatest variety of plant species on Earth.
            a   b

10. Nigel and Jack decided to cook macaroni and cheese for lunch.
           a   b

My score: ____ **10**

My time: ....
                           minutes   seconds

www.prim-ed.com   Prim-Ed Publishing®

Minute 55

Name: .... **Date:** ....

For Questions 1–5, use at least one prepositional phrase found in the box to write a sentence.

about four o'clock	across the street	in my space
against the wall	along the path	of the crowd
around the bend	behind the door	over the hill

1. ....

2. ....

3. ....

4. ....

5. ....

For Questions 6–10, circle the prepositional phrase in each sentence.

6. She put the present inside the box and posted it.

7. 'Please put all maths books on my desk', said Mrs Larmer.

8. She could barely see through the window.

9. Will you go to the party or will you go home?

10. Sarah walked on the footpath, facing traffic.

My score: ____ / 10   **My time:** ....
minutes   seconds

Minute 56

Name: .... **Date:** ....

For Questions 1–5, write the article a or an to correctly complete each phrase.

*(Hint: Use **a** before a word that begins with a consonant sound. Use **an** before a word that begins with a vowel sound.)*

1. .... fox and her babies

2. .... orange and a banana

3. .... honest answer

4. .... busy city

5. .... ancient scroll

For Questions 6–10, write the article(s) that best completes each sentence. (Use a, an or the.)

6. Melanie's team, the Stingrays, just scored three goals to win .... championship hockey game.

7. They played in .... championship tournament all week and had to beat

   .... good team to make it to the finals.

8. .... game was held on Sunday 28 September.

9. Billy saw .... opportunity to score in the last minutes of .... second half and succeeded.

10. It was .... great victory and .... honour to be declared the best team in the country.

My score: ____
10

My time: ....
                        minutes   seconds

Minute 57

Name: ....   **Date:** ....

For Questions 1–5, circle the correct conjunction to complete the sentence.

(Hint: A **conjunction** is a word that joins words or groups of words. It can show togetherness or contrast; for example: Patricia **and** Mark went to the restaurant, **but** Mark did not eat.)

1. The rain began, (yet/since/so) the ceremony was moved inside.

2. Albania is a small country, (and/since/or) it is one of Europe's poorest.

3. Sound travels fast. (Since/However/So), light travels faster.

4. Albert Namatjira was born near Alice Springs, Northern Territory, (so/although/ but) grew up in the Arrernte community.

5. Ancient Sumerians developed cuneiform, (and/or/since) Ancient Egyptians developed hieroglyphics.

For Questions 6–10, write a conjunction from the box to best complete each sentence. Do not use a conjunction more than once.

> and   yet   so   but   since   or   although   because

6. The new house was complete, ... it had no furniture.

7. Samantha .... Jessie are sisters.

8. The canteen served hamburgers .... not hot dogs.

9. My friend asked if I wanted to see either a comedy .... an action film.

10. .... the clown was somewhat funny, he also annoyed me.

My score:

10

My time: ....
minutes   seconds

Minute 58

Name: .... **Date:** ....

For Questions 1–4, rewrite the two sentences as a single sentence. Use a conjunction to join them.

(Hint: Eliminate words that repeat, and then combine the rest of the words to shorten sentences and save time.)

1. I will go to the park. I will get Jerome.

   ....

2. Veronica enjoys ballet. She doesn't like ballet recitals.

   ....

3. The guitarist played a quiet ballad. The singer hummed softly.

   ....

4. The internet can be a good source of information. The internet also provides entertainment.

   ....

For Questions 5–10, write yes if the example is a compound sentence. Write no if it is not.

5. Ponce de Leon explored the south-east coast of North America.   ....

6. I will take a weight training class and an aerobics class.   ....

7. He and I will take a trip down to France in the autumn or winter.   ....

8. Alexander Graham Bell invented the telephone.   ....

9. The teachers were ready for the start of school, but the pupils were not ready for the holidays to end.   ....

10. Icicles hung from the trees, and children made snowmen in the park.   ....

My score: _____
10

My time: ....
                        minutes   seconds

Name: ....   **Date:** ....

For Questions 1–5, underline the appositive in each sentence. Circle the noun or pronoun that it describes.

*(Hint: An **appositive** identifies or renames the words before it; for example: Our teachers,*
***Mr Jones and Ms Liddell**, went to a conference on Friday.)*

1. Lionel, the football star, is the most popular boy in school.

2. Dr Williams, my paediatrician, checked my reflexes with a small rubber hammer.

3. Our class finished reading *Charlie and the chocolate factory*, Roald Dahl's masterpiece, last week.

4. Is that your sister, Hannah, with the ponytail?

5. The Bathurst 1000 race, the epitome of Australian racing, was first held in 1960.

For Questions 6–10, write D if the underlined portion is a dependent clause. Write I if the underlined portion is an independent clause.

*(Hint: A **dependent clause** does not express a complete thought and is not a complete sentence on its own. An **independent clause** expresses a complete thought and could stand alone as its own sentence.)*

6. Come to my house, and <u>we will start on our science project.</u>   ....

7. All stations will televise the prime minister's speech <u>when he speaks.</u>   ....

8. My brother will drive us to the cinema <u>after he is finished at work.</u>   ....

9. The professor announced an exam, and <u>pupils scrambled to study.</u>   ....

10. Troy will enter the yodelling contest <u>if Maggie enters.</u>   ....

My score: _____
10

My time: ....
minutes   seconds

Minute 60

Name: .... **Date:** ....

Underline the prepositional phrase(s) in each sentence.

(Hint: The remaining words should still make a complete sentence.)

1. The entire class went to the performance except Charles.

2. Sailors used to use the stars to find their location on Earth.

3. Groovy girls in the 1960s wore their hair very long and very straight.

4. James Cook landed in New Zealand.

5. New Year's Day is a big celebration for our family.

6. Many companies in our community allow employees time off to vote.

7. Percussion instruments make sound when they are struck by the musician.

8. She closed the book and walked out of the library into the bright sunshine.

9. Nate grew up on a farm in Sutton.

10. The United Nations was founded in 1945, after World War II ended.

My score: **10**

My time: ....
minutes   seconds

Name: .... **Date:** ....

For **Questions 1–5**, write the article *a* or *an* *to correctly complete each phrase.*

1. .... kneepad

2. .... high-flying kite

3. .... biology class

4. .... hour

5. .... once-in-a-lifetime opportunity

For **Questions 6–10**, *circle the article that correctly completes each sentence.*

6. Hervey Bay Primary held three fundraisers to buy new computers for (the/an) computer room.

7. If you have any questions about (an/a) problem on the maths homework, please write which problem number it is in your journal.

8. Kevin displayed (an/the) coin he found at an old ghost town.

9. (An/A) PG-rated film is appropriate for all ages.

10. (An/A) bat flew in my bedroom window, making me scream.

My score: ——— **My time:** ....
10
minutes   seconds

Minute 62

Name: ....   **Date:** ....

For Questions 1–5, circle the conjunction that correctly completes each sentence.

1. I say I'm busy, (yet/and/or) I always find myself saying yes when people ask for help.

2. I turn my phone off at night (because/however/yet) I don't want to be disturbed.

3. The phone not only woke me up (and/yet/but also) woke up my sister.

4. Bring either a pen (but also/yet/or) a pencil.

5. I bought a new skirt (however/and/but also) a new jumper.

For Questions 6–10, circle the conjunctions that join two or more things. Underline the conjunctions that contrast two or more things (or that change the direction of the sentence).

6. We looked at the take-out menus and circled our food choices.

7. We always order fried rice, so this time we tried something different.

8. Do you want noodles or stir-fry?

9. Gemma likes soy sauce and pepper on all of her food.

10. Daniel eats a lot, although he always regrets it later.

My score: **10**

My time: ....
minutes   seconds

Minute 63

Name: .... **Date:** ....

For Questions 1–6, write yes if the example is a compound sentence. Write no if is not.

1. Valerie will visit Ireland to view the *Book of Kells*, but she will not have time to tour the countryside.   ....

2. Janet cut the cake, and we all sang 'Happy birthday'.   ....

3. Ashley and Nick felt upset when their football team lost.   ....

4. Air pollution is harmful to plants and to animals.   ....

5. Jennifer will join the chorus, and she will also take piano lessons this year.   ....

6. Chinese Australians and Korean Australians often celebrate the lunar new year.   ....

For Questions 7–10, rewrite the sentences as a single sentence.

7. At summer's end, many pupils pack up for university. They drive to their campuses.

   ....

8. The pizza was cut into eight pieces. It was all gone shortly thereafter.

   ....

9. The athletes in the triathlon run. The athletes also bike ride for kilometres. They also have to swim.

   ....

10. I know how to ride a bicycle. I also can ride a unicycle. My friend knows how to ride a bicycle and unicycle, too.

   ....

My score: ____ **My time:** ....

10

minutes   seconds

Minute 64

Name: .... **Date:** ....

For Questions 1–5, write a sentence using each of the appositives below.

my favourite book	a film released last week
my hardest subject in school	the tiny kitten
my sister's friend	

1. ....

2. ....

3. ....

4. ....

5. ....

For Questions 6–10, write D if the underlined portion is a dependent clause. Write I if the underlined portion is an independent clause.

6. My older sister goes to the café <u>where Wendy works</u>.   ....

7. Patrick earned extra pocket money by mowing lawns and <u>he planned to spend it on video games</u>.   ....

8. It was impossible to ignore <u>the terrible stench that came from the hallway</u>.   ....

9. The tree is withering and <u>losing its leaves already</u>.   ....

10. Brianna walked to Nancy's house and <u>together they went to the shopping centre</u>.   ....

My score:

10

My time: ....
minutes   seconds

Name: .... **Date:** ....

Add another word to the beginning or the end of each word below to create a compound word.

1. air ....

2. back ....

3. brain ....

4. day ....

5. dog ....

6. heart ....

7. counter ....

8. down ....

9. earth ....

10. man ....

My score: $\overline{10}$

My time: ....
minutes   seconds

Name: .... **Date:** ....

Write a synonym for each underlined word.

1. The <u>loud</u> blast from the car horn shook him awake.

    ....

2. Jack refused to be <u>afraid</u> of a tiny spider.

    ....

3. You are out if you step outside the <u>boundary</u>.

    ....

4. Dr Garrison was very <u>concerned</u> about Amber's high fever.

    ....

5. The <u>level</u> of the water continued to rise.

    ....

6. After lacrosse practice, my uniform is <u>dirty</u>.

    ....

7. The sunset was <u>pretty</u>.

    ....

8. A <u>bright</u> light filled the auditorium and the show began.

    ....

9. The wheatfields seem to go on <u>forever</u>.

    ....

10. It is best to fly a kite on a <u>windy</u> day.

    ....

My score: ____

10

My time: ....

minutes   seconds

Minute 67

Name: .... **Date:** ....

Write a synonym for each word.

1. smart   ....

2. narrow   ....

3. apart   ....

4. argue   ....

5. centre   ....

6. awful   ....

7. shy   ....

8. smelly   ....

9. cute   ....

10. path   ....

My score: $\dfrac{\quad}{10}$

My time: ....
                                 minutes   seconds

Minute 68

Name: ....   **Date:** ....

Draw a line to match each word with its antonym.

1. part   •   •   ancient

2. praise   •   •   whole

3. modern   •   •   slow

4. ceiling   •   •   rough

5. speedy   •   •   criticise

6. protected   •   •   subtract

7. add   •   •   intermittent

8. constant   •   •   unsheltered

9. asleep   •   •   floor

10. smooth   •   •   awake

My score: _____
10

My time: ....

minutes   seconds

www.prim-ed.com   Prim-Ed Publishing®

Name: .... **Date:** ....

Write an antonym for each word.

1. tardy   ....

2. new   ....

3. rotten   ....

4. scarce   ....

5. flat   ....

6. locked   ....

7. sink   ....

8. lazy   ....

9. empty   ....

10. dishonest   ....

My score: $\dfrac{}{10}$

My time: ....
                                 minutes   seconds

Name: .... **Date:** ....

For each sentence below, use the other form of the underlined homograph to write a new sentence.

(Hint: **Homographs** are words that are spelt the same, but have different meanings and often have different pronunciations.)

1. <u>Close</u> the screen door to keep the mosquitoes out.

   ....

2. Barry caught the biggest <u>bass</u> I've ever seen.

   ....

3. We watched the <u>dove</u> hover over her babies.

   ....

4. Where will we <u>house</u> the hamster?

   ....

5. The snake prefers to eat <u>live</u> mice.

   ....

6. Mrs Billings had to <u>separate</u> the two mischievous girls.

   ....

7. The weather forecaster <u>projects</u> rain for the weekend.

   ....

8. How can you mend a <u>tear</u> in the tent?

   ....

9. What is your <u>address</u>?

   ....

10. Johnny will <u>present</u> the award to Michelle.

   ....

My score: _____
10

My time: ....
                minutes   seconds

Name: .... **Date:** ....

Write the correct homophone to complete each sentence.

*(Hint: **Homophones** are words that sound the same but are spelt differently and have different meanings.)*

1. Vera .... seven cupcakes.
   ate   eight

2. What type of .... do you like to eat for breakfast?
   cereal   serial

3. We .... Tony and Elaine talking about the birthday party.
   herd   heard

4. The .... efficiently cleaned each room.
   maid   made

5. The actor studied her lines for the .... of Juliet.
   roll   role

6. Our school's .... wears a tie every day.
   principal   principle

7. The class gave a loud .... when the teacher announced a quiz.
   groan   grown

8. The teacher's helper .... around the papers.
   passed   past

9. I can't .... to watch.
   bear   bare

10. The boat appeared out of the ....
    mist   missed

My score: _____

10

My time: ....
minutes   seconds

Minute 72

Name: .... **Date:** ....

Circle the correct word in brackets to complete each sentence.

1. Irena went (too/to) the museum.

2. Brad and I saw (two/too) rabbits running through the forest.

3. Rene had chilli for lunch, (to/too).

4. (Too/Two) many pupils packed into the bus.

5. (There/They're) are no seats left.

6. Mary and Kristine went to get (their/they're) backpacks.

7. (They're/Their) winning the game.

8. (It's/Its) Renè's turn to play.

9. When (your/you're) finished with your dinner, please clear your plate.

10. The whale created a huge splash when it smacked (its/it's) flukes on the water.

My score: _____
10

My time: ....
minutes   seconds

Minute 73

Name: .... **Date:** ....

Write a synonym and an antonym for each word.

Word	Synonym	Antonym
1. tired	....	....
2. similar	....	....
3. noisy	....	....
4. receive	....	....
5. comical	....	....
6. increase	....	....
7. stroll	....	....
8. equal	....	....
9. valiant	....	....
10. grief	....	....

My score: $\dfrac{}{10}$

My time: ....
minutes   seconds

Name: .... **Date:** ....

For Questions 1–5, write the homograph to complete each sentence.

(Hint: The word is used in the sentence.)

1. Kylie will present Bridget with a ....

2. The nurse wound the bandage around the ....

3. We have one minute to find the .... details.

4. The contract states Harvey must not .... any contagious diseases.

5. Troops will not desert the army in the ....

For Questions 6–10, complete each sentence with a homophone from the box.

course/coarse	kernel/colonel	feet/feat
night/knight	allowed/aloud	

6. Deanne ran the .... without tipping any hurdles.

7. Only one .... was left in the popcorn popper.

8. It was an incredible .... to climb the rock wall.

9. The .... stormed the castle to save the damsel in distress.

10. Grandad .... me to use his fishing rod.

My score: ___

10

My time: ....
minutes   seconds

Negatives

Name: .... **Date:** ....

Write yes if the sentence is written correctly. Write no if it is not.

*(Hint: Negative words include **never, no, nobody, not, nowhere** as well as **barely, hardly, scarcely**. They also include any contractions with the word **not**.)*

1. I don't got no gum. ....

2. He won't want nothing to drink. ....

3. They have not had hardly anybody over to their house. ....

4. Stephanie don't never take the bus. ....

5. The gardener won't water the plants when it's night. ....

6. Mr Hoff can't barely see anything without his glasses. ....

7. Please don't forget to sign your name. ....

8. Nowhere do they not take that kind of credit card. ....

9. The parents told the children that they wouldn't go to Hamilton Island for their holidays. ....

10. Our dogs, Holly and Chas, are nowhere to be found. ....

My score:

10

My time: ....
　　　　　　　　　minutes 　　　　seconds

Minute 76

Name: .... **Date:** ....

For Questions 1–5, write the two words that combine to make each contraction.

1. they've ....

2. she'd ....

3. I'm ....

4. don't ....

5. hadn't ....

For Questions 6–10, write the contraction for each set of underlined words.

6. You will become a top-level player one day. ....

7. That shirt does not go with those trousers. ....

8. Let us go to the library tomorrow. ....

9. Who would like to see a film tonight? ....

10. Peter will not finish the race. ....

My score: $\dfrac{}{10}$

My time: ....
minutes   seconds

Name: .... **Date:** ....

For Questions 1–5, insert commas in the correct places.

1. Poh please remember to buy milk butter and eggs.

2. Yes I would like chips with my hamburger.

3. Marie Curie a Nobel Prize winner was a physical chemist.

4. Cyclones can happen anytime but they are most common between November and April.

5. An insect's body is divided into the head thorax and abdomen.

For Questions 6–10, write yes if all necessary commas are included and in the correct place. Write no if they are not.

6. My aunt Eileen is moving to Cardiff, Wales. ....

7. 'It's time for ballet class', declared Mum. ....

8. On, 6 May 1937, the *Hindenburg* burst into flames upon descent. ....

9. Noah quietly asked, 'Who is the bus driver?' ....

10. The harbour bridge was opened in Sydney, Australia. ....

My score: _____
10

My time: ....
minutes   seconds

Minute 78

Name: .... **Date:** ....

Cross out the unnecessary negative words. Write other words on the line to replace them if needed.

1. I don't have no plans for the weekend. ....

2. There isn't no peanut butter in the cupboard. ....

3. I can't hardly believe Shelly would dye her hair purple. ....

4. The water couldn't barely trickle through the thick reeds. ....

5. Lily can't never go to the park. ....

6. There is not hardly any water left in my bottle. ....

7. Why isn't nobody cleaning up the living room? ....

8. I didn't do nothing. ....

9. There isn't nothing to do during the long summer months. ....

10. We aren't never going to do nothing. ....

My score: _____ / 10

My time: ....
minutes   seconds

Minute 79

Name: ....   **Date:** ....

Insert commas to correctly complete each sentence.

1. Tony Hawk was born 12 May 1968 in San Diego USA.

2. Tokyo Japan is one of the world's most populous cities.

3. Jayden said 'You make the best chocolate pudding in the world'.

4. The Kennedy Space Centre is located in Orlando Florida.

5. 'I watched the funniest programme on television' Michael said.

6. Until the bridge is completed we will have to cross at the crossroads down the street.

7. Angella replied 'We've already eaten Mum'.

8. Robert will you please answer questions three four and five for us?

9. Keisha the tallest girl in the class balanced herself carefully on a chair and pinned the picture to the bulletin board.

10. My three favourite Olympic sports are swimming basketball and gymnastics.

My score: _____
10

My time: ....
minutes   seconds

Name: .... Date: ....

Add a prefix to change the meaning of each word and write its new definition.
Use each prefix in the box only once.

| anti- | dis- | fore- | inter- | mis- |
| non- | over- | re- | sub- | trans- |

Root word	Definition	Word with prefix	Definition
1. sense	good judgement	...............sense	....
2. eat	consume	...............eat	....
3. sight	see	...............sight	....
4. handle	manage	...............handle	....
5. view	look at	...............view	....
6. septic	infection	...............septic	....
7. agree	think alike	...............agree	....
8. national	of a country	...............national	....
9. marine	water	...............marine	....
10. port	place	...............port	....

My score: _____

10

My time: ....

minutes   seconds

Minute 81

Name: .... **Date:** ....

Use the definition to add a suffix to each root word. Use each suffix in the box only once.

-ment	-en	-or	-est	-ful
-ic	-less	-able	-ous	-y

Root word	Word with suffix	Definition
1. afford	....	can pay for
2. courage	....	characterised by bravery
3. hope	....	having much faith
4. sharp	....	most pointed
5. wood	....	made of wood
6. poet	....	showing characteristics of a poet
7. act	....	a person who acts
8. move	....	act of moving
9. help	....	unable to aid
10. fruit	....	having the essence of fruit

My score: $\dfrac{}{10}$

My time: ....
minutes seconds

Minute 82

Name: .... Date: ....

Draw a line from the Greek or Latin root to its meaning. Draw another line from
the meaning to the sample word.

Root	Meaning	Sample word
1. dent •	• hear •	• graphic
2. aud •	• see •	• dentures
3. bio •	• trust •	• microscope
4. cred •	• take •	• biology
5. circ •	• tooth •	• vocal
6. graph •	• writing •	• circulate
7. prim •	• call •	• audio
8. voc •	• life •	• primary
9. cap •	• around •	• capture
10. scope •	• first •	• credible

My score:
_____
10

My time: ....
minutes   seconds

Prim-Ed Publishing®

Minute 83

Name: .... **Date:** ....

For Questions 1–5, underline the Greek or Latin root(s) in each word.

1. dentist

2. biochemistry

3. circular

4. auditorium

5. telescope

For Questions 6–10, circle the prefix and/or suffix in each word.

6. antibiotic

7. manageable

8. submerge

9. homeless

10. enjoyment

My score: $\dfrac{}{10}$

My time: ....
minutes   seconds

Name: .... **Date:** ....

For Questions 1–4, underline the complete subject and circle the complete predicate in each sentence.

1. Babies cry.

2. The swimmers raced to the finish line.

3. The city of Los Angeles hosted the 1984 Summer Olympic Games.

4. A rusty old car sat abandoned on the side of the road.

For Questions 5–7, write yes if the group of words is a complete sentence. Write no if it is not.

5. A cool glass of water. ....

6. Football practice is every Monday and Wednesday. ....

7. In the morning, after the sun has risen. ....

For Questions 8–10, insert the correct punctuation at the end of each sentence. Write what type of sentence it is: declarative, interrogative, imperative or exclamatory.

8. What day is it ....

9. Go away ....

10. The humidity weighed heavily on everyone ....

My score: _____
10

My time: ....
minutes   seconds

Name: .... **Date:** ....

For Questions 1–3, underline the common nouns. Circle the proper nouns.

1. Seoul is the capital of South Korea.

2. When we went snorkelling in Vanuatu, we saw a lot of fish.

3. The Tigers are my favourite rugby team.

For Questions 4–7, write each noun in plural form.

4. manuscript ....

5. sketch ....

6. dragonfly ....

7. woman ....

For Questions 8–10, rewrite each phrase in possessive form.

8. The pens belonging to the pigs ....

9. The howl of the wind ....

10. The kerbs of the streets ....

My score: _____

10

My time: ....
minutes   seconds

Name: .... **Date:** ....

For Questions 1–2, replace the underlined word(s) with a pronoun.

1. <u>Claude</u> enjoys riding his bike and playing tennis.   ....

2. <u>Paula and I</u> went fishing at the stream.   ....

For Questions 3–7, circle the correct pronoun to complete each sentence.

3. Mr Price asked Laura and (I/me) to deliver the package.

4. The blue and red skateboards belong to (we/us).

5. Tracy brought flowers for (her/she) and me.

6. (He/Him) and (I/me) will go to school on the bus.

7. I brought a release form for (her/she) so she could attend the excursion.

For Questions 8–10, circle the pronoun in each sentence.

8. Everyone will make a ceramic bowl.

9. Will somebody please answer the door?

10. Anyone can play on the volleyball team.

My score: _____

10

My time: ....
                 minutes   seconds

Minute 87

Name: .... **Date:** ....

For Questions 1–5, replace the underlined word(s) with a pronoun.

1. The tabby cat cleaned <u>the tabby cat's</u> paw. ....

2. Jason and Brenda put on <u>Jason and Brenda's</u> uniforms. ....

3. We can fit two cars in <u>my family's</u> garage. ....

4. Lee always listens to <u>Mr Daley's</u> radio programme in the morning. ....

5. Angus wrote an essay and handed in <u>Angus's</u> paper in the morning. ....

For Questions 6–10, circle the correct pronoun to complete each sentence.

6. 'Kevin and Travis, keep your comments to ....'.
   yourselves   yourself

7. The football fans showed their support by dressing .... in club colours.
   yourselves   themselves

8. We looked at .... in the photograph.
   ourselves   ourself

9. The man sat by .... on the bench in the park.
   itself   himself

10. When Jenna fell on the rocks, she injured .... badly.
    herself   themselves

My score: $\dfrac{}{10}$

My time: ....
                      minutes   seconds

Name: .... **Date:** ....

For Questions 1–2, underline the verb in each sentence.

1. Melville Fresh greengrocer sells four different types of orange.

2. The Dutch swimmer is the winner.

For Questions 3–6, write each verb in past-tense form.

Present tense	Past tense
3. begin	....
4. expect	....
5. wear	....
6. decide	....

For Questions 7–10, circle the correct verb to complete each sentence.

7. Please (lay/lie) your bag on the bench.

8. The villagers (sit/set) outside their homes in the evenings.

9. The sun (raises/rises) in the east.

10. The date to return the rented DVDs has (passed/past).

My score: _____
10

My time: ....
minutes   seconds

Name: .... Date: ....

For Questions 1–5, circle the correct verb form to complete each sentence.

1. Cats .... chasing mice and birds.
   enjoy   enjoys

2. Ken and James .... excellent writers.
   is   are

3. Dad .... into the empty parking space.
   pull   pulls

4. There .... dozens of bicycles locked in the rack.
   were   was

5. Daisy .... to finish her book review tonight.
   hope   hopes

For Questions 6–10, circle the correct pronoun to complete each sentence.

6. Girls can store PE kit in (their/her) lockers.

7. Pilots must train extensively before earning (their/his) licences.

8. Any girl who finishes early may work on (her/their) homework.

9. The doctors finished (their/his) rounds and went home.

10. We ran away fast when we saw the skunk lift (their/its) tail.

My score: _____

10

My time: ....
minutes   seconds

Minute 90

Name: ....   **Date:** ....

Circle the correct form of the adjective to complete each sentence.

1. Chocolate ice-cream is (more good/better) than vanilla.

2. The Wanderers are the (worse/worst) team in the entire league.

3. The Bucking Bronco roller-coaster is (more exciting/most exciting) than the Free Fall ride.

4. Which jar has (most/more) coffee?

5. The (most creative/more creative) designer in the contest will win a new car.

6. The overhead light is the (brighter/brightest) light in the entire room.

7. It is (more colder/colder) in Dublin than in Madrid.

8. That is the (weirder/weirdest) insect I've ever seen.

9. The pupil with the (most clever/cleverest) idea will win the prize.

10. A gold medal is awarded to the (most good/best) contestant in the Academic Decathlon.

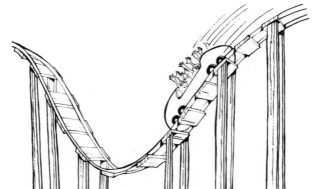

My score: ____ / **10**

My time: ....
                         minutes   seconds

Minute 91

Name: .... Date: ....

For Questions 1–5, circle the word the underlined adverb modifies.

1. Jonah waited <u>eagerly</u> for his appointment.

2. The boat bounced <u>roughly</u> on the wide blue sea.

3. The ballerina twirled <u>daintily</u> on her pointe shoes.

4. Bring it <u>tomorrow</u>.

5. Raindrops trickled <u>slowly</u> down the windowpane.

For Questions 6–10, write what question the underlined adverb answers: how, when, where, how often or to what degree.

6. Monica exercises <u>regularly</u>.   ....

7. Mrs Petersen said to put the boxes <u>here</u>.   ....

8. Dogs barked <u>noisily</u> as we rode past.   ....

9. Charge the battery <u>fully</u> before using.   ....

10. The wind blew the rain <u>sideways</u>.   ....

My score: __10__

My time: ....
                minutes   seconds

Name: .... **Date:** ....

For Questions 1–3, write either between or among to correctly complete each sentence.

1. The race will be .... Jerome and Taylor.

2. It is difficult to choose .... the many flavours.

3. Cross the street .... the signs at the zebra crossing.

For Questions 4–10, circle the preposition(s) in each sentence.

4. The television in the living room is still not working.

5. The table under the window provides the best light for reading.

6. Gravel crunched under our feet as we walked up the driveway.

7. Maria poured juice into a tall glass.

8. Bart will play the lead role, Julius Caesar, in the school play.

9. Darlene waited all day for the dough to rise.

10. Walk around the lake and stop at the path's end.

My score: ____
10

My time: ....
minutes   seconds

www.prim-ed.com   Prim-Ed Publishing®

Name: .... **Date:** ....

For Questions 1–3, underline the appositive in each sentence. Circle the noun phrase or pronoun it describes.

1. Wendy, my older sister, attends Willowbrook Secondary School.

2. The prime minister, a well-respected man, made the decision to raise taxes.

3. The first woman to scale Mt Everest, Junko Tabei of Japan, accomplished a remarkable achievement.

For Questions 4–7, write D if the underlined clause is a dependent clause or I if the clause is an independent clause

4. The red roses in <u>Mrs Rueben's garden</u> are so beautiful in the summer. ....

5. Our team won the basketball game and <u>we felt proud of our success</u>. ....

6. Maddy makes jewellery and <u>she often gives it to her friends</u>. ....

7. Mum hung blue curtains in my bedroom <u>to block the morning light</u>. ....

For Questions 8–10, write a dependent clause to make each sentence a complex sentence.

8. The temperature outside is very cold ....

9. Wash thoroughly with soap ....

10. The newspaper reported a robbery ....

My score: ____

10

My time: ....
  minutes   seconds

Minute 94

Name: .... **Date:** ....

Write yes *if the sentence is written correctly*. Write no *if it is not*.

1. We don't got any money to buy a cinema ticket. ....

2. It's so foggy I can't barely see anything. ....

3. We could not go to the park because it was raining. ....

4. Lisa and Benjamin don't never miss hockey practice. ....

5. Pacific Avenue is nowhere around here. ....

6. Our mother just told us that we did not have to clean the living room. ....

7. She don't have no pen I can borrow. ....

8. Do not forget to close the door behind you. ....

9. I was not going to not do my homework. ....

10. I have not seen Mary anywhere. ....

My score: ____
10

My time: ....
minutes   seconds

Apply your grammar knowledge

Name: .... **Date:** ....

Write a synonym and an antonym for each word.

Word	Synonym	Antonym
1. precious	....	....
2. messy	....	....
3. alike	....	....
4. many	....	....
5. sharp	....	....
6. active	....	....
7. dangerous	....	....
8. quiet	....	....
9. wide	....	....
10. brave	....	....

My score: $\overline{\quad\quad}$
10

My time: ....
minutes   seconds

Minute 96

Name: .... Date: ....

For Questions 1–5, complete each sentence with the correct homophone from the box.

reign/rein/rain	pear/pair	plain/plane
ceiling/sealing	guest/guessed	

1. When the .... began, Lindsey opened her umbrella.

2. The .... was painted a bright blue.

3. Alex sliced the .... and brought it to the table.

4. The pupils .... how many buttons were in the jar.

5. The animals roamed the Kenyan ....

For Questions 6–10, write the homograph to complete each sentence.

(Hint: The word is used in the sentence.)

6. I object to having that .... in my backpack.

7. Can you please place your .... in the recycling bin?

8. The spring rains have made the .... water plentiful.

9. What can you produce from the items in the .... section of the grocery store?

10. Who will conduct the orchestra if her .... is unacceptable?

My score: ——— **My time:** ....
                  10   minutes   seconds

Apply your grammar knowledge

Name: .... Date: ....

For Questions 1–5, add a suffix to change the meaning of each word. Use each suffix in the box only once.

| -ness | -ible | -ish | -ly | -en |

1. sincere....................

2. bright....................

3. quick....................

4. self....................

5. flex....................

For Questions 6–10, add a prefix to each word and write its definition. Use each prefix in the box only once.

| pre- | un- | in- | im- | dis- |

Word with prefix   **Definition**

6. ....similar   ....

7. ....comfortable   ....

8. ....fix   ....

9. ....visible   ....

10. ....possible   ....

My score: _____
10

My time: ....
                minutes   seconds

Minute 98

Name: .... **Date:** ....

For Questions 1–4, draw a line from the Latin or Greek root to its meaning. Draw another line from the meaning to the sample word.

Root	Definition	New word
1. ology •	• study of •	• biography
2. port •	• water •	• geology
3. aqua •	• writing •	• portable
4. graph •	• to carry •	• aquarium

For Questions 5–7, add a prefix to change the meaning of each word. Use the prefixes in the box.

5. ....port

6. ....word

7. ....wind

| re- | fore- | trans- |

For Questions 8–10, add a suffix to change the meaning of each word. Use the suffixes in the box.

8. graph...................

9. flavour...................

10. profess...................

| -ful | -or | -ic |

My score: ___ **10**

My time: .... minutes .... seconds

Apply your grammar knowledge

Name: .... Date: ....

Circle all the words that need to be capitalised in each sentence.

1. Russell Street is a street located near Federation square in Melbourne, victoria.

2. At the time of Federation, Melbourne was the largest city in australia. Before moving to canberra, it was also the nation's capital from 1901 to 1927.

3. The royal Exhibition Building in carlton Gardens was home to Australia's first parliament.

4. Australia's most famous sporting event, the Melbourne cup, is held on the first Tuesday in november at a racetrack in flemington.

5. Many other well known sporting events occur in Melbourne, including the Australian open, the Australian grand Prix and the Australian football League's grand final.

6. The city has also hosted the olympics Games (in 1956) and the Commonwealth games (in 2006).

7. Opening in 1884, flinders street Station is one of the city's great landmarks and icons.

8. The city's queen victoria Market is the largest open-air market in the southern Hemisphere.

9. The city is located on Port phillip Bay, with the yarra River flowing through it.

10. It is the second most populous city in Australia. Only the capital of New south wales, Sydney, is larger.

My score: _____ 10

My time: ....
minutes   seconds

Minute 100

Name: .... Date: ....

Insert commas and end punctuation in the correct places in each sentence.

1. The tropical rainforests of South America Africa and South-East Asia are always warm and wet

2. Many animals such as birds and bats live in the rainforests

3. Did you know many animals in the tropical rainforest live in trees

4. Mum said 'Pack up kids we're going to Water World'

5. An hour later there were eight of us in the van

6. The trip to Water World takes over an hour so we sang songs on the way

7. We went on the junior slides the taller slides and the slippery slope but no-one dared go on the Wild Riot

8. 'That was the most fun I've ever had' exclaimed Robert

9. 'Can we go again' asked Vanessa

10. Later after all of us were in bed we talked about all of the fun we had

My score: _____
10

My time: ....
minutes   seconds

Minute answer key

Minute 1
1. C 6. C
2. I 7. I
3. I 8. C
4. C 9. C
5. I 10. I

Minute 2
1. Ella
2. squid
3. stars
4. Petronas Towers
5. phones
6. painted
7. is
8. sway
9. is awarded
10. came

Minute 3
1. My sister, Lindsey
2. The brand-new building
3. Alex's sister
4. The primary school pupils
5. The eager group of tourists
6. put his books in my backpack
7. is a fun winter sport
8. helped the flowers bloom
9. politely handed me my receipt
10. will take her place

Minute 4
1. Jess and Emmelene
2. roses and daisies
3. Jumpers, coats and rugs
4. The goal defence and the wing defence
5. The United States, Canada and Mexico
For Questions 6–10, answers will vary. Sample answers include:
6. wiped
7. splashed
8. downloaded
9. washes
10. pack

Minute 5
1. circle: Look at that! underline: Isn't that a gorgeous sunset?
2. circle: I can't believe I missed the bus! underline: What will I do now?
3. circle: It's unbelievable! underline: Was that your fastest swim record?
4. circle: I can't believe it's broken! underline: How long will it be before we can get it repaired?

5. !, . ,?
6. !, ?
7. ?, !, . or !
For Questions 8–10, answers will vary. Sample answers include:
8. I'm so hungry!
9. Please lower your voices!
10. You really have to try this!

Minute 6
1. I 6. I
2. D 7. D
3. I 8. I
4. I 9. I
5. D 10. D

Minute 7
1. . 6. .
2. ? 7. !
3. . 8. .
4. ! 9. .
5. ? 10. ?

Minute 8
1. . 6. I
2. . 7. I
3. . 8. .
4. I 9. I
5. . 10. I

Minute 9
1. S 6. S
2. P 7. S
3. P 8. P
4. P 9. S
5. P 10. P

Minute 10
1. circle: virus underline: A virus
2. circle: great Egyptian pyramids underline: The great Egyptian pyramids
3. circle: Heather and Tony underline: My good friends, Heather and Tony
4. circle: robin underline: The bright red robin
5. circle: hot chocolate underline: The steaming hot chocolate
For Questions 6–10, answers will vary. Sample answers include:
6. Martin walked to school and pulled open the school doors.
7. All plants use oxygen and take in water.
8. My mother washed and curled her hair.
9. Many Brazilians love to watch and play football.
10. Rachel strolled along the footpath and

looked at the view.

Minute 11
1. ., D 6. ., IMP
2. ?, I 7. ., D
3. !, E 8. ?, I
4. ., IMP 9. !, E
5. ?, I 10. ., D

Minute 12
Order of answers within each category may vary.
Person
1. explorer
2. veterinarian
3. woman
Place
4. city
5. park
6. post office
Thing or idea
7. bread
8. love
9. bucket
10. friendship

Minute 13
1. underline: friends circle: Jeff, Creswick Camp
2. underline: glove circle: Javier
3. underline: match circle: Botanic Park
4. underline: pupils, causes circle: First World War
5. underline: ingredients circle: Steven
6. underline: house circle: Nick's
7. underline: teacher circle: Parkes Observatory
8. underline: day circle: Byron Secondary School
9. underline: prime minister circle: UK, Downing Street
10. underline: pictures circle: Venus

Minute 14
1. Brazil
2. Budapest
3. Chinese
4. Diwali
5. Eiffel Tower
6. Torah
7. Muslims
8. Vatican City
9. Juanita
10. Bolte Bridge

Minute 15
1. shoes
2. heroes
3. boxes
4. skates
5. monkeys
6. companies

7. princesses
8. cherries
9. witches
10. chimneys

Minute 16
1. children, places
2. photos, deer
3. dishes, potatoes
4. babies, feet
5. sheep, hills
6. pens, shelves
7. leaves, piles
8. friends, quizzes
9. doors, elves
10. films, biographies

Minute 17
1. The spider's web
2. Teresa's biscuit
3. Kenneth's flute
4. The pupil's lunch
5. The doctor's stethoscope
6. The child's father
7. Ahn's shoes
8. The map's key
9. The team's mascot
10. The writer's biography

Minute 18
1. The boys' team
2. The teachers' lounge
3. The ships' captains
4. The shops' computers
5. The children's classroom
6. The women's dresses
7. The partners' projects
8. The leaves' colours
9. The oxen's harnesses
10. The deer's hooves

Minute 19
1. He 6. us
2. They 7. her, me
3. She 8. us
4. He 9. her, me
5. They 10. him, me

Minute 20
1. myself
2. himself
3. yourselves
4. itself
5. ourselves
6. her
7. my, his
8. Whose
9. mine
10. Your

Minute 21
1. who
2. that
3. who
4. that
5. who
6. Anyone
7. anything
8. somebody
9. everyone

Minute answer key

10. Each

Minute 22
1. they are
2. their
3. her
4. his
5. their
6. its
7. their
8. their
9. they are
10. they

Minute 23
1. underline: sandwich
   circle: Charlene
2. underline: guitar
   circle: Melody Music
   Shop
3. underline: birthday
   circle: Parker's, January
4. underline: race
   circle: Tour de France,
   France
5. underline: cinema
   circle: Monday
6. underline: squirrel, trees
   circle: Highland Park
7. underline: apartment,
   floor
   circle: None
8. underline: banker, loan
   circle: Louise
9. underline: None
   circle: Statue of Liberty,
   New York City
10. underline: rubbish
    circle: None

Minute 24
For Questions 1–5, order of
answers may vary.
1. climbers
2. knives
3. utensils
4. months
5. people
6. beetles
7. hobbies
8. mice
9. halves
10. echoes

Minute 25
1. men's department
2. Cindy's bookshelf
3. galleries' windows
4. toddler's crayons
5. runners' water bottles
6. underline: Melissa's
   motorcycle
   circle: friends'
   motorcycles
7. underline: Dad's day
   circle: Dolphins' victory
8. underline: Jessica's
   allergies
   circle: flowers' pollen
9. underline: Daria's
   Grocery Store
   circle: dogs' loud
   barking
10. underline: Lisa's pet
    hamster
    circle: sofas' slippery

cushions

Minute 26
1. me
2. her
3. them
4. her, him
5. him, me
6. He
7. It
8. It
9. They
10. We

Minute 27
1. his
2. Their or His or Her or Our
3. their
4. her
5. our
6. himself
7. herself
8. themselves
9. yourself
10. itself

Minute 28
1. who
2. that
3. that
4. that
5. who
6. no
7. yes
8. no
9. no
10. yes

Minute 29
Answers for second verb will
vary.
1. soars, flies
2. drives, travels
3. sparkle, twinkle
4. leaps, bounds
5. skate, blade
6. cuts, gathers
7. lost, misplaced
8. sails, floats
9. swims, explores
10. hit, batted

Minute 30
1. is
2. am
3. are
4. are
5. were
6. a
7. b
8. b
9. b
10. a

Minute 31
1. sailed
2. screamed
3. flew
4. answered
5. grew
6. acted
7. wore
8. wrote
9. boiled
10. broke

Minute 32
1. invented
2. hunted
3. joking
4. mentioned
5. moving
6. offering
7. ruled
8. planning
9. unloading

10. visiting

Minute 33
1. lay
2. lies
3. set
4. sit
5. rise
6. raised
7. lay
8. passed
9. sat
10. lay

Minute 34
1. I laugh, You laugh, She
   laughs, They laugh
2. I ask, You ask, He asks,
   They ask
3. I start, You start, It starts,
   They start
4. I paint, You paint, He
   paints, They paint
5. I dance, You dance,
   She dances, They
   dance
6. mop
7. plants
8. stings
9. turns
10. ignores

Minute 35
1. is
2. earns
3. is
4. are
5. are
6. are
7. are
8. drives
9. wear
10. are

Minute 36
1. circle: raced
2. circle: collapses
3. underline: was
4. circle: built
5. underline: is
For Questions 6–10, answers
will vary. Sample answers
include:
6. The rain fell from the
   dark sky.
7. The sun is shining down
   on the buildings.
8. My friend and I
   laughed and danced
   at the concert.
9. Lisa yawned and
   stretched.
10. My stomach grumbled
    loudly.

Minute 37
1. H
2. L
3. L
4. H
5. H
6. H
7. L
8. H
9. L
10. L

Minute 38
1. ran
2. dove
3. froze
4. walked
5. thought
6. sweeping
7. dried
8. marching
9. stretched

10. exploded

Minute 39
1. lay
2. lie
3. set
4. passed
5. raise
6. yes
7. no
8. no
9. yes
10. no

Minute 40
1. expects
2. flops
3. were
4. are
5. plans
6. is
7. wishes
8. eats
9. are
10. uses

Minute 41
1. awkward
2. magic
3. delicious
4. tiny, black, white
5. dirty, smelly
6. unpredictable
7. beautiful
8. demanding
9. little, green
10. mashed

Minute 42
1. helpful or kind
2. dangerous
3. exquisite
4. speedy
5. plump or immense
6. contented
7. level
8. helpful or kind
9. immense
10. playful

Minute 43
1. smoother
2. fresher
3. more general
4. more difficult
5. more jealous
6. kinder
7. lighter
8. more memorable
9. quicker
10. more helpless

Minute 44
1. best
2. worse
3. more
4. less
5. worse
6. flatter, flattest
7. braver, bravest
8. stronger, strongest
9. calmer, calmest
10. leaner, leanest

Minute 45
1. mightily

Minute answer key

2. heavily
3. eagerly
4. exactly
5. crazily
6. good
7. well
8. good
9. well
10. well

Minute 46
1. how
2. how often
3. to what degree
4. when
5. where
6. when
7. how
8. how
9. how often
10. to what degree

Minute 47
1. faster, fastest
2. more quietly, most quietly
3. earlier, earliest
4. more often, most often
5. more slowly, most slowly
6. farther, farthest
7. nearer, nearest
8. more carefully, most carefully
9. sooner, soonest
10. more gracefully, most gracefully

Minute 48
1. harder
2. larger
3. louder
4. smallest
5. tallest
6. best
7. worse
8. least
9. fewer
10. most

Minute 49
1. ate
2. held
3. go
4. held
5. considered
6. sat
7. spoke
8. marched
9. generous
10. remember

Minute 50
1. adv
2. adj
3. adv
4. adj
5. adv
6. adv
7. adj
8. adj
9. adj

10. adv

Minute 51
1. seat
2. shone
3. view
4. rhythm
5. runs
6. signs
7. climbed
8. bounced
9. worked
10. traveller

Minute 52
1. between, as
2. with, inside
3. at, across
4. at, after
5. beside, up
6. inside
7. near
8. beneath
9. with
10. Since

Minute 53
1. between
2. among
3. between
4. between
5. between
6. no
7. yes
8. no
9. yes
10. no

Minute 54
1. a
2. b
3. b
4. b
5. a
6. b
7. a
8. b
9. b
10. b

Minute 55
For Questions 1–5, answers will vary.
6. inside the box
7. on my desk
8. through the window
9. to the party
10. on the footpath

Minute 56
1. a   6. the
2. an   7. the, a
3. an   8. The
4. a   9. an, the
5. an   10. a, an

Minute 57
1. so
2. and
3. However
4. but

5. and
For Questions 6–10, answers will vary.
6. yet
7. and
8. but
9. or
10 Although

Minute 58
For Questions 1–4, answers will vary. Sample answers include:
1. I will go to the park and get Jerome.
2. Veronica enjoys ballet, although she doesn't like ballet recitals.
3. The guitarist played a quiet ballad, and the singer hummed softly.
4. The internet can be a good source of information and entertainment.
5. no
6. no
7. no
8. no
9. yes
10. yes

Minute 59
1. underline: the football star
   circle: Lionel
2. underline: my paediatrician
   circle: Dr Williams
3. underline: Roald Dahl's masterpiece
   circle: *Charlie and the chocolate factory*
4. underline: Hannah
   circle: sister
5. underline: the epitome of Australian racing
   circle: Bathurst 1000 race
6. I
7. D
8. D
9. I
10. D

Minute 60
1. to the performance
2. on Earth
3. in the 1960s
4. in New Zealand
5. for our family
6. in our community
7. by the musician
8. of the library, into the bright sunshine
9. on a farm, in Sutton
10. in 1945, after World War II ended

Minute 61

1. a   6. the
2. a   7. a
3. a   8. the
4. an   9. A
5. a   10. an

Minute 62
1. yet
2. because
3. but also
4. or
5. and
6. circle: and
7. underline: so
8. underline: or
9. circle: and
10. underline: although

Minute 63
1. yes   4. no
2. yes   5. yes
3. no   6. no
For Questions 7–10, Answers will vary. Sample answers include:
7. At summer's end, many pupils pack up for university and drive to their campuses.
8. The pizza was cut into eight pieces, and it was all gone shortly thereafter.
9. The athletes in the triathlon run, bike ride for kilometres, and swim.
10. My friend and I know how to ride a bicycle and a unicycle.

Minute 64
Questions 1–5, answers will vary.
6. D
7. I
8. D
9. D
10. I

Minute 65
Answers will vary. Sample answers include:
1. airport
2. backtrack
3. brainstorm
4. someday
5. doghouse
6. sweetheart
7. countertop
8. downtown
9. earthquake
10. manhole

Minute 66
Answers will vary. Sample answers include:
1. noisy
2. fearful
3. limit
4. worried
5. height
6. filthy

Minute answer key

7. gorgeous
8. gleaming
9. endlessly
10. breezy

Minute 67

Answers will vary. Sample answers include:
1. intelligent
2. thin
3. separated
4. fight
5. middle
6. terrible
7. bashful
8. stinky
9. adorable
10. trail

Minute 68

1. whole
2. criticise
3. ancient
4. floor
5. slow
6. unsheltered
7. subtract
8. intermittent
9. awake
10. rough

Minute 69

Answers will vary. Sample answers include:
1. early
2. ancient
3. fresh
4. plentiful
5. mountainous
6. unlocked
7. rise
8. diligent
9. full
10. trustworthy

Minute 70

Answers will vary. Sample answers include:
1. I live close to school.
2. The bass from the stereo made the house shake.
3. Gerald dove from the board into the water.
4. Our house is two storeys tall.
5. We need food and water to live.
6. The girls had separate rooms.
7. This year in science we have two major projects.
8. After he slammed his finger in the door, his eyes began to tear up.
9. The president of the company came to

address the crowd.
10. For my birthday, the only present I want is a skateboard.

Minute 71

1. ate
2. cereal
3. heard
4. maid
5. role
6. principal
7. groan
8. passed
9. bear
10. mist

Minute 72

1. to
2. two
3. too
4. Too
5. There
6. their
7. They're
8. It's
9. you're
10. its

Minute 73

Answers will vary. Sample answers include:
1. synonym: exhausted antonym: energetic
2. synonym: alike antonym: dissimilar
3. synonym: loud antonym: quiet
4. synonym: accept antonym: give
5. synonym: funny antonym: serious
6. synonym: enlarge antonym: lessen
7. synonym: saunter antonym: scurry
8. synonym: same antonym: imbalanced
9. synonym: brave antonym: cowardly
10. synonym: sadness antonym: elation

Minute 74

1. present
2. wound
3. minute
4. contract
5. desert
6. course
7. kernel
8. feat
9. knight
10. allowed

Minute 75

1. no
2. no
3. no
4. no
5. yes
6. no
7. yes
8. no
9. yes
10. yes

Minute 76

1. they have
2. she had or she would

3. I am
4. do not
5. had not
6. You'll
7. doesn't
8. Let's
9. Who'd
10. won't

Minute 77

1. Poh, please remember to buy milk, butter and eggs.
2. Yes, I
3. Marie Curie, a Nobel Prize winner, was
4. anytime, but
5. head, thorax
6. yes
7. yes
8. no
9. yes
10. yes

Minute 78

Answers will vary. Sample answers include:
1. no, any (or, no without an additional word)
2. no, any
3. can't, can (or, hardly)
4. barely (or, couldn't, could)
5. never, (or, can't, can)
6. not
7. nobody, anybody
8. nothing, anything
9. nothing, anything (or, isn't, is)
10. never, nothing, anything (or, aren't are, nothing, anything)

Minute 79

1. Tony Hawk was born 12 May 1968, in San Diego, USA.
2. Tokyo, Japan, is one of the world's most populous cities.
3. Jayden said, 'You make the best chocolate pudding in the world'.
4. The Kennedy Space Centre is located in Orlando, Florida.
5. 'I watched the funniest programme on television', Michael said.
6. Until the bridge is completed, we will have to cross at the crossroads down the street.
7. Angela replied, 'We've already eaten, Mum'.
8. Robert, will you please answer questions three, four and five for us?
9. Keisha, the tallest girl in

the class, balanced herself carefully on a chair and pinned the picture to the bulletin board.
10. My three favourite Olympic sports are swimming, basketball and gymnastics.

Minute 80

Answers will vary. Sample answers include:
1. nonsense, making no sense
2. overeat, consume too much
3. foresight, see before
4. mishandle, manage badly
5. review, to look at again
6. antiseptic, against infection
7. disagree, not think alike
8. international, among nations
9. submarine, underwater
10. transport, carry to another place

Minute 81

1. affordable
2. courageous
3. hopeful
4. sharpest
5. wooden
6. poetic
7. actor
8. movement
9. helpless
10. fruity

Minute 82

1. dent, tooth, dentures
2. aud, hear, audio
3. bio, life, biology
4. cred, trust, credible
5. circ, around, circulate
6. graph, writing, graphic
7. prim, first, primary
8. voc, call, vocal
9. cap, take, capture
10. scope, see, microscope

Minute 83

1. dent
2. bio, chem
3. circ
4. aud
5. tele, scope

Minute answer key

6. anti-, -ic
7. -able
8. sub-
9. -less
10. -ment

Minute 84
1. underline: Babies
    circle: cry
2. underline: The
    swimmers
    circle: raced to the
    finish line
3. underline: The city of
    Los Angeles
    circle: hosted the
    1984 Summer Olympic
    Games
4. underline: A rusty old
    car
    circle: sat abandoned
    on the side of the road
5. no
6. yes
7. no
8. ?, interrogative
9. !, exclamatory
10. ., declarative

Minute 85
1. underline: capital
    circle: Seoul, South
    Korea
2. underline: snorkelling,
    fish
    circle: Vanuatu
3. underline: team
    circle: Tigers
4. manuscripts
5. sketches
6. dragonflies
7. women
8. pigs' pens
9. wind's howl
10. streets' kerbs

Minute 86
1. He
2. We
3. me
4. us
5. her
6. He, I
7. her
8. Everyone
9. somebody
10. Anyone

Minute 87
1. its
2. their
3. our
4. his
5. his
6. yourselves
7. themselves
8. ourselves
9. himself
10. herself

Minute 88

---

1. sells
2. is
3. began
4. expected
5. wore
6. decided
7. lay
8. sit
9. rises
10. passed

Minute 89
1. enjoy
2. are
3. pulls
4. were
5. hopes
6. their
7. their
8. her
9. their
10. its

Minute 90
1. better
2. worst
3. more exciting
4. more
5. most creative
6. brightest
7. colder
8. weirdest
9. cleverest
10. best

Minute 91
1. waited
2. bounced
3. twirled
4. Bring
5. trickled
6. how often
7. where
8. how
9. to what degree
10. how

Minute 92
1. between
2. among
3. between
4. in
5. under, for
6. under, up
7. into
8. in
9. for
10. around, at

Minute 93
1. underline: my
    older sister
    circle: Wendy
2. underline: a well-
    respected man
    circle: The prime
    minister
3. underline: Junko
    Tabei of Japan
    circle: The first woman
    to scale Mt Everest
4. D
5. I
6. I
7. D
*For Questions 8–10, answers
will vary. Sample answers
include:*
8. The temperature
    outside is very cold
    when it's winter.
9. Wash thoroughly with

---

soap before handling
food.
10. The newspaper
    reported a robbery in
    the west part of town.

Minute 94
1. no
2. no
3. yes
4. no
5. yes
6. yes
7. no
8. yes
9. no
10. yes

Minute 95
*Answers will vary. Sample
answers include:*
1. synonym: prized
    antonym: worthless
2. synonym: cluttered
    antonym: neat
3. synonym: same
    antonym: dissimilar
4. synonym: numerous
    antonym: few
5. synonym: spiky
    antonym: blunt
6. synonym: energetic
    antonym: idle
7. synonym: hazardous
    antonym: safe
8. synonym: silent
    antonym: loud
9. synonym: broad
    antonym: narrow
10. synonym: heroic
    antonym: spineless

Minute 96
1. rain
2. ceiling
3. pear
4. guessed
5. plain
6. object
7. can
8. spring
9. produce
10. conduct

Minute 97
1. sincerely or sincereness
2. brighten, brightness,
    or brightly
3. quickness, quicken,
    or quickly
4. selfish
5. flexible
*For Questions 6–10, answers
will vary. Sample answers
include:*
6. dissimilar, not the same
7. uncomfortable, not at
    ease
8. prefix, something set
    before
9. invisible, not able
    to be seen
10. impossible, not able
    to do

Minute 98
1. study of, geology
2. to carry, portable
3. water, aquarium
4. writing, biography
5. transport

---

6. foreword
7. rewind
8. graphic
9. flavourful
10. professor

Minute 99
1. Square, Victoria
2. Australia, Canberra
3. Royal, Carlton
4. Cup, November,
    Flemington
5. Open, Grand,
    Football
6. Olympics, Games
7. Flinders, Street
8. Queen, Victoria,
    Southern
9. Phillip, Yarra
10. South, Wales

Minute 100
1. The tropical
    rainforests of South
    America, Africa and
    South-East Asia are
    always warm and
    wet.
2. Many animals, such
    as birds and bats, live
    in the rainforests.
3. Did you know many
    animals in the
    tropical rainforest live
    in trees?
4. Mum said, 'Pack up,
    kids. We're going to
    Water World!'
5. An hour later, there
    were eight of us in
    the van.
6. The trip to Water
    World takes over an
    hour, so we sang
    songs on the way.
7. We went on the
    junior slides, the
    taller slides and the
    slippery slope, but no
    one dared go on the
    Wild Riot.
8. 'That was the most
    fun I've ever had!'
    exclaimed Robert.
9. 'Can we go again?'
    asked Vanessa.
10. Later, after all of us
    were in bed, we
    talked about all of
    the fun we had.